European Agency for Safety and Health at Work

WORKING ENVIRONMENT INFORMATION

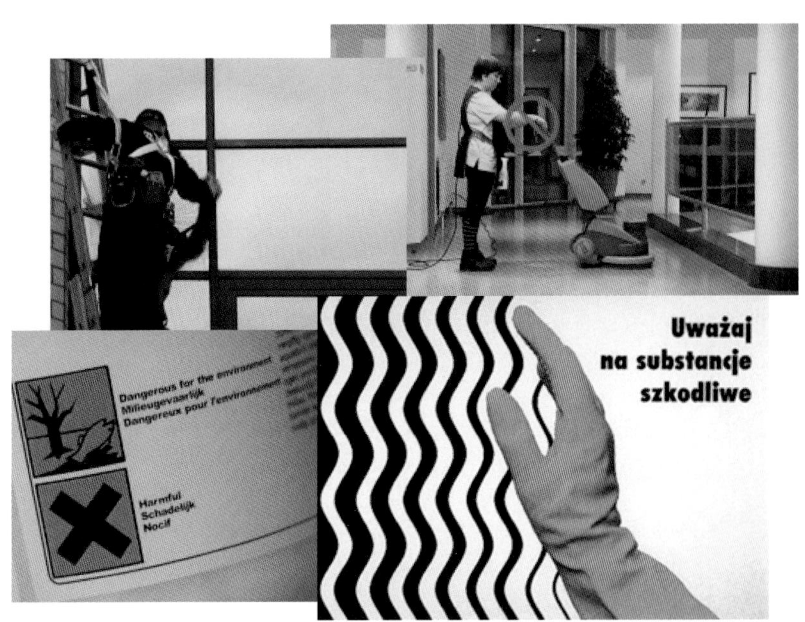

Preventing harm to cleaning workers

Preventing harm to cleaning workers

Authors
Tim Tregenza — EU-OSHA — European Agency for Safety and Health at Work, Spain

Topic Centre Working Environment:
Bernd Preuß, Harald Wilhelm, Jochen Pfeil, Reinhard Rheker, Uwe Musanke — Berufsgenossenschaft der Bauwirtschaft (BG BAu), Germany
Beata Oleszek, Magdalena Galwas, Małgorzata Gołofit-Szymczak — Centralny Instytut Ochrony Pracy Państwowy Instytut Badawczy (CIOP-PIB), Poland
José Miquel Martin Cabeças — Faculdade de Ciências e Tecnologia da Universidade Nove de Lisboa (DEMI), Portugal
Spiros Dontas — Elliniko Institoyto Ygienis Kai Asfaleias Tis Ergasias (ELINYAE), Greece
Marie-Amélie Buffet — Groupement de l'Institution Prévention de la Sécurité Sociale pour l'Europe — (EUROGIP), France
Francesca Grosso — Instituto Superiore per la Prevenzione e la Sicurezza del Lavoro (ISPESL), Italy
Katariina Röbbelen-Voigt, Klaus Kuhl, Lothar Lißner — Kooperationsstelle Hamburg (KOOP), Germany
Karen Muylaert, Lieven Eeckelaert, Nele Roskams — Institut pour la Prevention et le bien-être au travail/ Instituut voor Preventie en Welzijn op het Werk (PREVENT), Belgium

Edited by:
Joanna Kosk-Bienko — EU-OSHA — European Agency for Safety and Health at Work, Spain

Reviewed and approved by:
Terence N. Taylor, Head of the Working Environment Information Unit — European Agency for Safety and Health at Work — (EU-OSHA), Spain

EU-OSHA would like to thank its Focal Point network and the Sectoral Social Dialogue Committee on industrial cleaning for their valuable input and feedback.

Cover photos:
1. „Be careful – Dangerous substances", Artists: Igor Banaszewski, Monika Wojtaszek.
Courtesy of the Occupational Safety Poster Competiton organised by the Central Institute for Labour Protection – National Research Institute, Poland.

Europe Direct is a service to help you find answers to your questions about the European Union

Freephone number (*):

00 800 6 7 8 9 10 11

(*) Certain mobile telephone operators do not allow access to 00 800 numbers, or these calls may be billed.

More information on the European Union is available on the Internet (http://europa.eu).

Cataloguing data can be found at the end of this publication.

Luxembourg: Office for Official Publications of the European Communities, 2009

ISBN 978-92-9191-259-9
doi:10.2802/10668

Printed in Luxembourg

PRINTED ON WHITE CHLORINE-FREE PAPER

CONTENTS

CONTENTS

List of figures, tables and pictures

List of figures, tables and pictures

Foreword

In February 2007 the European Commission published a new Community strategy on health and safety at work which aims to reduce occupational accidents in the EU by 25 %. The strategy notes that some categories of workers are still overexposed to occupational risks, some types of companies are more vulnerable, and some sectors are still particularly dangerous.

The strategy encourages the exchange of good practice as part of the approach to reducing the number and cost of accidents and ill health in Europe and it is to this that this report seeks to contribute.

Thanks go to all our European partners, particularly the Focal Points, the Sectoral Social Dialogue Committee for the cleaning sector, and the Topic Centre Working Environment staff who have contributed to the preparation of this report.

Jukka Takala

Director

European Agency for Safety and Health at Work

August 2009

Executive summary

Cleaning is carried out in every workplace. In some industries, such as the food and catering sectors, poor cleaning can cause a business to fail. Cleaning is an essential task and, when done well, it can reduce both costs to the company and the risks to workers' safety and health by, for example, extending the life of workplace equipment and keeping floor surfaces in good condition. Sadly though, cleaning tasks have a bad image as it is a task associated with dirt and waste; workers are sometimes looked down on and their work taken for granted.

The cleaning industry itself has been a dynamic and growing economic sector across Europe, providing jobs for many workers. While there are some very large cleaning companies in Europe, the sector is dominated by small businesses — many with fewer than 10 workers. The industry has an active and prominent social dialogue at the European level that provides leadership to the sector.

This report considers the challenges to be overcome in improving the safety and health of cleaners, and examines actions taken to achieve this goal. By its nature, the report focuses on challenges associated with cleaning tasks, seeking solutions to these challenges that can reduce the risks to workers' health and safety. This should not obscure the positive developments in this field, and it should be noted that the European cleaning industry bodies representing both employers and workers are leading the way in improving the performance of the sector.

The tendency for cleaning work to be contracted out with tenders considered on the basis of price alone means that there is heavy pressure on cleaning companies to cut costs. This can result in an inadequate investment in training and other management activities essential for worker protection. As labour costs tend to make up the bulk of the costs of a cleaning business, there is a risk that unscrupulous employers may seek an unfair advantage in tendering by resorting to illegal employment practices such as not paying full social insurance costs or hiring illegal labour. Good procurement practice — considering value for money rather than just the price — benefits all concerned: client companies, cleaning enterprises, and workers.

The poor perception of cleaning and cleaning workers can discourage the effective management of cleaning services, by both the employer and, where contracted out, the client. Related to this poor perception of cleaning work is that it is often carried out by women, by part-time workers, and by workers who are migrants or from ethnic minorities.

Cleaning is often done outside normal working hours, frequently in the early morning, evening or night. The workers may be employed on part-time and temporary contracts and are often doing more than one job. Such working patterns can increase risks to worker health and safety. While in some workplaces cleaning cannot be carried out during normal business hours, often it can be — a change that can benefit the cleaning company, the cleaner and the client.

Cleaning work is seldom seen as a core activity in businesses. This can result in a lack of awareness of the hazards and risks associated with cleaning and so a failure to carry out an adequate risk assessment and implement protective measures.

Common hazards, risks, and health outcomes include:

- risk of slips, trips and falls, particularly during 'wet work';
- exposure to dangerous ingredients in cleaning materials;

- exposure to hazardous substances being cleaned, which can include biological hazards such as moulds or human wastes;
- psychosocial issues including work-related stress, violence and bullying;
- risk of musculoskeletal disorders;
- risks, such as electric shock, from work equipment.

The work-related health disorders found in cleaners include:

- musculoskeletal disorders;
- work-related stress, anxiety and sleeping disorders;
- skin diseases such as contact dermatitis and eczema;
- respiratory disorders including asthma;
- cardiovascular diseases.

Where cleaning work is contracted out, there can be additional difficulties as the client company and the cleaning company need to liaise and share knowledge to ensure that risks are identified and eliminated or controlled.

The messages in this report can be summarised as follows:

- select your cleaning service by value, not price;
- switch to daytime cleaning;
- value the cleaners and the work they do — if it is done wrong, it can cost the business;
- see cleaning as an essential task which can expose the workers to particular hazards and risks;
- assess the risks to cleaning workers and implement preventive measures;
- share knowledge with all relevant parties, including the client company, the cleaning contractor and the workers themselves.

1.

INTRODUCTION

The cleaning industry is one of the largest and most dynamic service sectors in the European Union. Rapidly developing technological processes require rapidly developing maintenance and cleaning procedures.

Cleaning is a generic job — it is carried out in all industry groups and all workplaces, outside and inside, including public areas. Cleaning is needed in every sector of the economy, and thus cleaners are better defined by task rather than by sector. Common tasks are surface cleaning, including mopping, dusting, vacuuming, polishing of floors and work surfaces and routine housekeeping. Cleaners have to cope with changing workplaces, surfaces and cleaning materials, yet they are perceived as being 'only cleaners', with their qualifications and experience disregarded. But choosing the right cleaning agents, equipment and procedures is important to guarantee an extended life of buildings, fittings, office equipment and furniture.

Who is covered in this report?

This report covers common cleaning tasks carried out in workplaces such as hotels, hospitals, catering establishments, and offices. Many of these tasks are carried out by workers employed by cleaning companies contracted in by a client to provide cleaning services. While day-to-day cleaning activities in the industrial sectors are also covered, the report does not look at workshop activities such as parts cleaning, degreasing and maintenance work, street cleaning, domestic cleaning, and window cleaning.

1.1. Changes and challenges in the cleaning sector

According to an industry survey [1], over three million workers are employed in the European cleaning industry, and the overall number of both cleaners and cleaning contractors (i.e. companies offering cleaning services to other businesses) is rising. While there are a few large companies in the field, the sector is dominated by small businesses, most of which employ fewer than 10 workers. Despite initiatives in some Member States, cleaning tends to be performed outside normal working hours, either in the early morning or the evening. The workforce in the cleaning sector tends to be part-time, female-dominated, and with a high proportion of migrant workers and workers from ethnic minorities. Rationalisation in the cleaning sector, with a view to

1 The Cleaning Industry in Europe — an EFCI Survey 2006 Edition (Data 2003). The European Federation of Cleaning Industries, Brussels, Belgium (http://www.feni.be). For the purpose of this survey, 'cleaning industry' has to be understood in reference to the NACE classification — REV. 1, Section K, Division 74, Group 74.7: 'industrial cleaning'. It also includes some other activities carried out by cleaning contractors, such as waste management services, chimney sweeping, building façade cleaning, or maintenance of areas around buildings.

improving productivity, reducing costs and adapting to technological development, has led to increasing competition and subcontracting in the sector; changes that can have an impact on the occupational safety and health of workers[2].

1.1.1. Competition and subcontracting

Unfair competition is a problem in the cleaning sector. Clandestine or undeclared employment, the limited financial resources required to set up a cleaning company, the non-existence of barriers to limit access to the profession and the fact that customers generally opt for the cheapest solution, are the main reasons for the fierce competition within the sector.

The phenomenon of competition is linked to the tendency to subcontract out cleaning services. This outsourcing of cleaning work seems to impose certain strong constraints (as regards costs, quality, hours, etc.) and clients appear to base their business decisions on price alone, without taking into account issues such as safety and health requirements, quality criteria, or even the security or trustworthiness of a contractor.

The main expense involved in operating a cleaning business is labour, which amounts to around 80 % of costs invoiced to the customer (the percentage varies across the Member States). It follows that, to gain a competitive advantage, labour costs have to be kept as low as possible. Problems arise particularly if some contractors do not respect employment and social security requirements, so driving down the market price; legitimate companies that invest for the long term through training and staff development can then be forced out of the market.

This pressure on labour costs can have an impact on workers' safety and health, through non-compliance with safety and health requirements (e.g. training) to cut costs, placing greater workloads on the cleaners (using fewer workers for the same work), and obliging cleaners to work with unsafe, unhealthy or inadequate equipment and materials.

These measures can expose workers to:

- risk of accidents (e.g. through unsafe work equipment);
- chemical risks (e.g. having to work with dangerous chemicals when a safer alternative is available);
- biological risks (e.g. through lack of training on risks from handling 'sharps');
- an increased risk of violence (if a cleaner has to work alone due to low staff levels);
- work-related stress, for example through high workloads, working alone, bullying by employers to get work done more quickly, or long working hours.

2 Commission of the European Communities Directorate-General for Employment and Social Affairs, elaboration of a European training manual in the field of health and safety for workers in the cleaning sector, sectoral study, UNI-Europa — FENI/EFCI, June 2000.

A large European research project[3] noted:

- many cleaners were exposed to risk factors for musculoskeletal disorders, such as working in constrained positions, heavy lifting, monotonous work, and a rapid pace of work;
- a high cardiorespiratory load on cleaning workers;
- skin problems linked to 'wet work' and the use of cleaning agents;
- allergies and asthma reported amongst cleaning workers;
- poor ergonomic design of buildings, facilities and furniture, as well as cleaning equipment and methods, impedes productive and quality cleaning and exposes the workers to health risks;
- risks related to psychosocial and physical work and the environment are common — cleaners have little or no control over their work and few opportunities to develop in their career;
- there is evidence to suggest that the physical strain of cleaning can be reduced through improved ergonomic planning, better organisation of work and enhancement of the cleaner's individual resources.

1.1.2. Perceptions of cleaning work

The cleaning industry suffers from a negative public perception of cleaning work and a certain distaste for it because of its association with dirt and waste. This can be aggravated by discrimination, for example by gender or ethnicity, or harassment and denial of workers' rights[4]. All of these are interrelated and can lead not only to direct physical injuries but also to stress-related health problems.

Thus it becomes clear that to improve the health and safety of cleaners in general, it is not sufficient to just follow the usual tracks of occupational safety and health but also to address issues such as workload, working time and schedules, work organisation, communication, qualifications, career opportunities and job satisfaction.

Procurement practice is a key factor in determining these issues for cleaning workers. This has been recognised by the social partners in the cleaning sector, who have produced a guide to help in the procurement process[5].

As will become clear in this report, the implementation of preventive measures in a holistic sense not only benefits the cleaning workers — who are healthier, have an improved perception of themselves, and are better qualified — but also results in a better quality service to the client, and improved effectiveness of cleaning companies through greater efficiency, better work organisation, reduced staff turnover and reduced absenteeism[6].

---

3 See final project report: Krueger, Detlef, Louhevaara, Veikko, Nilsen, Jette, Schneider, Thomas (eds), Risk Assessment and Preventive Strategies in Cleaning Work, Werkstattberichte aus Wissenschaft + Technik. Wb 13, Hamburg, 1997. The project is also presented online (http://www.rzbd.fh-hamburg.de/~prbiomed/risk_assessment.html and http://www.ttl.fi/Internet/English/Information/Electronic+journals/Tyoterveiset+journal/1999-02+Special+Issue/06.htm).

4 Arhan Virdi, 'A Victim at Work?' in European Cleaning Journal (http://www.europeancleaningjournal.com/index.php?option=com_content&task=view&id=289&Itemid=61).

5 UNI-Europa (Union Network International) and EFCI (European Federation of Cleaning Industries); Selecting best value — A guide for organisations awarding contracts for cleaning services (http://ec.europa.eu/employment_social/dsw/public/actRetrieveText.do?id=10242).

6 Huth, Elke, Krueger, Detlef, Zorzi, Gerlinde, Gesundheitsförderung im Krankenhausbetrieb — Funktionsbereich Reinigung, Abschlußbericht, Fachhochschule Hamburg, 1996. Huth, Elke,

1.1.3. Managing occupational safety and health

Cleaning has never been a particularly healthy and safe job, but now that tasks formerly done in-house are being outsourced on a large scale by both private and public organisations, managing the safety and health of cleaning workers is more complex than ever. Communication has become more difficult because it now has to involve the client, the occupants of the building, the cleaning service provider, and the cleaning workers themselves.

Since office staff and cleaners hardly meet, communication has to reach the latter via their managers, supervisors or representatives. But many cleaners complain of a lack of contact with their superiors. Language problems also play a role as migrants, ethnic minorities and the less qualified make up a large part of the cleaning workforce.

Many cleaners work alone to cover their share of the building. Being cut off from social interaction adds to their low self-perception, which is perpetuated by several unfavourable conditions:

- most cleaners are women and tend to regard their work as 'nothing special';
- most are unqualified or hardly qualified;
- in general there is no sophisticated equipment in use;
- many cleaning workers have language problems (e.g. migrants);
- many cleaning jobs are part-time (although the workers concerned may prefer to work full-time);
- work often takes place at unfavourable times;
- career prospects are few and courses to improve qualifications are seldom offered;
- low pay is widespread, so that sometimes cleaners need a second job to earn a living;
- cleaners are excluded from normal company life;
- dealing with dirt and waste is a 'low status' activity in the eyes of the public.

Company management should consider all these issues carefully, with clients and service providers coordinating their efforts in the area of occupational safety and health to improve conditions for cleaning staff. Responsibilities have to be clear, and risk assessments carried out and information shared as required by national legislation derived from European directives. This is relevant to both the 'host' workplace employer and the cleaning service provider. The hazards have to be listed, and risks to workers identified and evaluated. The varying levels of education and qualification among the workers concerned, as well as their communication skills (e.g. language) and physical abilities should be taken into account during this process.

Communication is of crucial importance as discussions between all stakeholders will provide a solid basis for tackling almost all relevant risks. Cleaning during the daytime will automatically facilitate direct contact between cleaners and office staff and thus greatly enhance communication. As will be seen in some case studies and policy initiatives described later in this report, this will not only improve the health and safety situation for the cleaners but also create a new feeling of being respected that will help them develop a better self-image. Worker retention can also be greatly improved, allowing experience and qualifications to build up, providing a better service to the client while preserving the health of the cleaners.

Krueger, Detlef, Kopf, Thomas, Gestaltung Gesunder Artbeitsbedingungen: Projekt Reinigung, Gesundheitsförderung für die Mitarbeiterinnen des Referates Technik und Hausverwaltung im Hygiene Institut Hamburg, Fachhochschule Hamburg, 2001.

The social partners at European level issued a joint declaration on daytime cleaning [1], stating: 'In this context, daytime cleaning is a term used to describe the restructuring of a contract in such a way as to provide for the operational requirements of the client but also to increase the proportion of hours delivered during the normal working day. Experiences in certain Member States have shown that the development towards daytime cleaning is perceived as positive on the whole for clients as well as for contractors and employees. Especially in the Scandinavian countries, daytime cleaning has been constantly increased — with the acceptance of the industry.'

1 The social dialogue in the cleaning sector: UNI-Europa (Union Network International) and EFCI (European Federation of Cleaning Industries); Joint declaration on daytime cleaning (http://www.union-network.org/unipropertyn.nsf/2aca427bf4dd1055c125719c004b7986/$FILE/DaytimeCleaningDeclaration.pdf).

But preventive measures can begin even before a cleaning service has been put into operation. When advertising for bids or inviting tenders for cleaning jobs, clients should 'ensure that they are selecting a provider to carry out cleaning functions who can combine quality with a favourable price rather than settling for the lowest price bidder' [7]. Quality relies on a qualified, experienced, and healthy staff. Service providers should be encouraged and given the chance to establish and continuously improve preventive measures. All stakeholders will profit and the dynamism of the cleaning sector can be utilised. This point is illustrated by some best practice case studies and policy initiatives described later on in this report.

The hazards and risks faced by cleaning workers vary depending on the premises being cleaned. For example, the type of workplace will dictate what:

- waste materials are being handled (e.g. sawdust from carpentry shops, blood in hospitals);
- surfaces are being cleaned (e.g. concrete floors in factories, marble in office foyers);
- substances are used to clean (e.g. bleaches and solvents);
- equipment will be used to do the cleaning.

7 UNI-Europa (Union Network International) and EFCI (European Federation of Cleaning Industries); Selecting best value — A guide for organisations awarding contracts for cleaning services (http://ec.europa.eu/employment_social/dsw/public/actRetrieveText.do?id=10242).

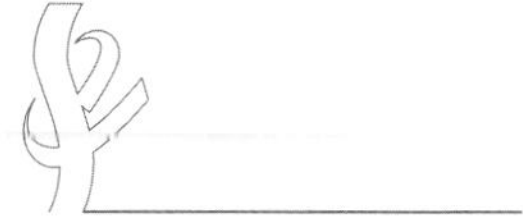

European Agency for Safety and Health at Work

WORKING ENVIRONMENT INFORMATION

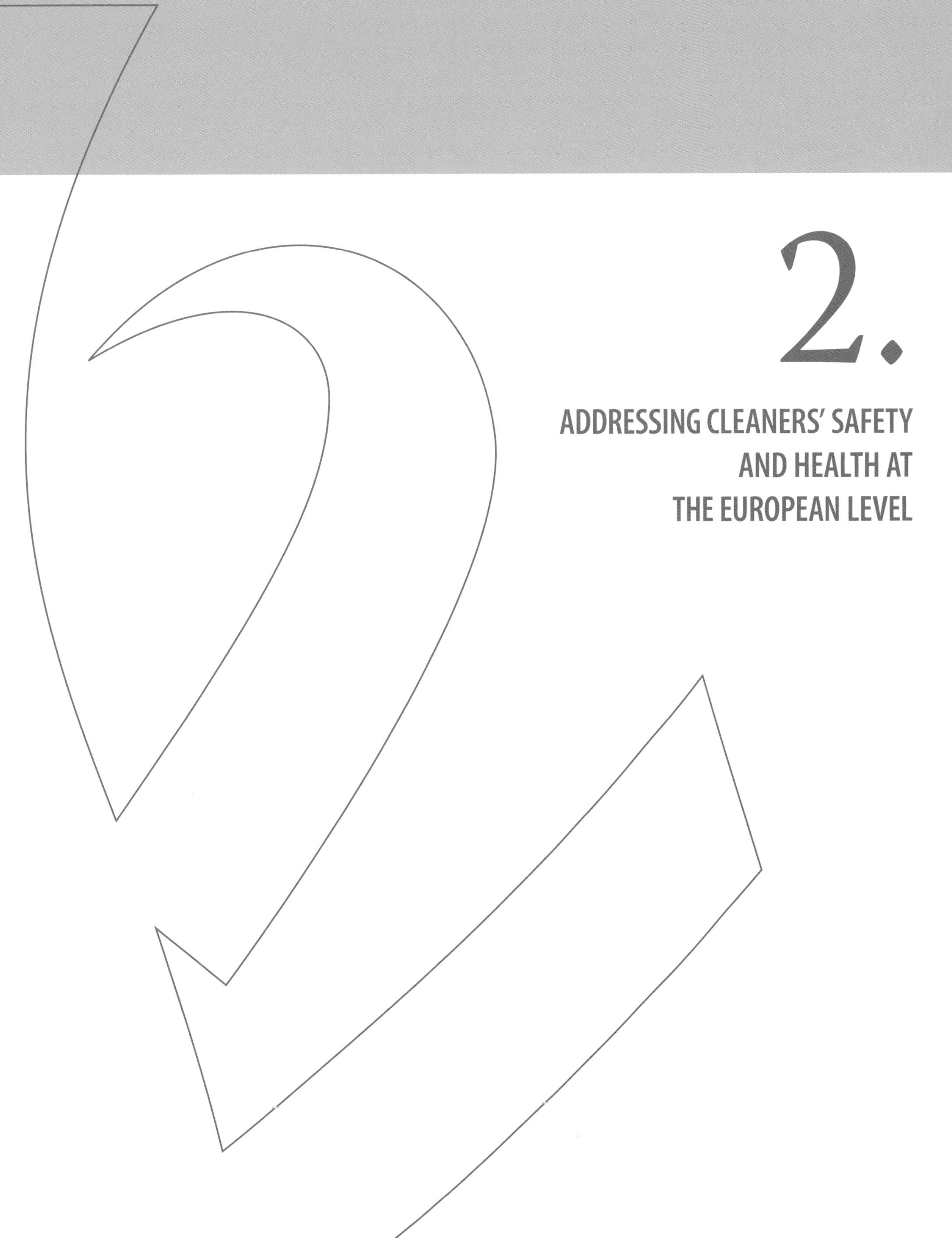

2.

ADDRESSING CLEANERS' SAFETY AND HEALTH AT THE EUROPEAN LEVEL

At the European level, action is being taken to reduce the risks to cleaning workers, not only through the approach of having a goal-setting European strategy and setting minimum legislative standards for occupational safety and health but also through research, social partnership, networking, and standard setting.

This diverse approach is required as the economic structure of the cleaning industry, the perceived low socioeconomic status of cleaning workers, and the impact of migration policies can all affect the level of risk facing cleaning workers.

2.1. The Community strategy 2007–12 on health and safety at work

In February 2007 the European Commission published a new Community strategy on health and safety at work. The strategy[8] [9] seeks a 25 % reduction in occupational accidents in the EU. It sets out a series of actions at European and national levels in the following main areas.

- Improving and simplifying legislation and enhancing its implementation in practice through non-binding actions such as exchange of best practice, awareness-raising campaigns and better information and training.
- Defining and implementing national strategies adjusted to the specific context of each Member State. These strategies should target the sectors and companies most affected and fix national targets for reducing occupational accidents and illness.
- Mainstreaming of health and safety at work in other national and European policy areas (education, public health, and research) and finding new synergies.
- Identifying and assessing potential new risks more efficiently through research, exchange of knowledge and practical application of results.

2.2. Legislation at European level

At European level, several directives have been published to improve safety and health at the workplace. Most of them can be classified under the framework Directive

8 Brussels, 21.2.2007 COM(2007) 62 final communication from the Commission to the European Parliament, the Council, the European Economic and Social Committee and the Committee of the Regions; Improving quality and productivity at work: Community strategy 2007–12 on health and safety at work (http://eurlex.europa.eu/LexUriServ/site/en/com/2007/com2007_0062en01.pdf).

9 '25 % cut in accidents at work by 2012 — new EU strategy' (http://ec.europa.eu/employment_social/emplweb/news/news_en.cfm?id=209).

89/391/EEC of 12 June 1989[10] and its offshoots. 'On the introduction of measures to encourage improvements in the safety and health of workers', the directive obliges employers to take the necessary measures to ensure the safety and health of workers in all aspects of their work. The provisions of these directives are enacted through national law in each Member State.

Of special interest in the cleaning sector, where the working conditions and control measures may be the responsibility of more than one employer (i.e. the service provider and its various clients) is Article 6.4: 'Where several undertakings share a workplace, the employers shall cooperate in implementing the safety, health and occupational hygiene provisions and, taking into account the nature of the activities, shall coordinate their actions in matters of the protection and prevention of occupational risks, and shall inform one another and their respective workers and/or workers' representatives of these risks'[11].

Some standards may also apply to cleaners. They give detailed technical information on the organisation of workplaces and equipment. For example, standards related to vibration exposure should be observed to protect cleaners from fatigue and disorders resulting from exposure to vibration.

All the workplace occupational safety and health directives and related national laws in all EU Member States request employers and employees to follow general principles of prevention:

- avoiding risk;
- evaluating risks which cannot be avoided;
- combating risks at source;
- adapting the work to the individual, especially as regards the design of the workplace, the choice of work equipment and the choice of working methods, with a view to alleviating monotonous, unduly arduous or fast-paced work;
- adapting to technical progress;
- replacing dangerous substances with non-dangerous or less dangerous ones;
- developing a coherent overall prevention policy which covers technology, organisation of work, working conditions, social relationships and the working environment;
- giving collective protective measures priority over individual protective measures;
- giving appropriate instructions to employees.

In addition, there exist directives on procurement that may also influence the working conditions of cleaners. These are listed in the annexes of this report.

10 Council Directive 89/391/EEC of 12 June 1989 on the introduction of measures to encourage improvements in the safety and health of workers at work (http://eur-lex.europa.eu/smartapi/cgi/sga_doc?smartapi!celexapi!prod!CELEXnumdoc&lg=en&numdoc=31989L0391&model=guichett).

11 This provision is also taken up in more specific rules and regulations like the German BG rule A1 2005 'Basis of Prevention', 2.5 and the Hazardous Substances Ordinance, 2004, paragraph 17. The rule and ordinance stipulate that there must be a coordinator if there is the possibility of a mutual risk for the employees of the client and the cleaning contractor.

2.3. Sectoral Social Dialogue, cleaning industry

European social dialogue in the cleaning sector dates back to 1992 and the Sectoral Social Dialogue Committee [12] (SSDC) was established in 1999. In this dynamic and growing sector, the social partners tackle specific issues in the sector by developing social dialogue and issuing guidance for all stakeholders, whether at a national or regional level.

The social partners have adopted common positions on employment, undeclared work, and vocational training. In 2004, they adopted joint recommendations addressed to industrial cleaning companies, their employees, their customers (both public and private sector) and public authorities (European, national and local). These recommendations relate in particular to promoting professionalism (through improved vocational training), staff retention (by promoting full-time and daytime work and by improving employee health and safety), combating discrimination and promoting social integration.

The agreements and texts signed by European organisations participating in all social dialogues potentially cover 70 million workers and nearly six million businesses in Europe. Owing to the incorporation of agreements into sectoral or business agreements, and the existence and use in many countries of extension procedures or similar practices and mechanisms, the rate of coverage for agreements is about 80 %. This percentage varies depending on the country, from around 30 % in the United Kingdom to approximately 95 % in Austria and Finland [13].

The committee has issued several documents.

- Regular annual surveys on the cleaning industry in Europe [14].
- A declaration on daytime cleaning as a contribution to the EU Lisbon strategy for more and better jobs. Experience from the Scandinavian countries in particular shows that daytime cleaning is perceived as largely positive for clients as well as for contractors and employees, producing a better response to clients' requirements, better possibilities for training and qualification and greater dignity for workers [15].
- A procurement guide [16] outlining the advantages of basing selection procedures on the economically most advantageous tender rather than the lowest price. Contractors often have to present bids so low they detrimentally affect quality, working conditions and staff training, and may even lead to illegal and unprofessional practices. The social dialogue partners call on authorities to follow

12 http://ec.europa.eu/employment_social/social_dialogue/sectorial12_en.htm

13 The sectoral social dialogue in Europe: Employment & social affairs — Industrial relations and industrial change, European Commission, Directorate-General for Employment and Social Affairs, manuscript completed in December 2002, available as a PDF document (http://ec.europa.eu/employment_social/publications/2003/ke4702397_en.pdf).

14 The Cleaning Industry in Europe — An EFCI Survey, 2006 Edition (Data 2003), Edited and published by the European Federation of Cleaning Industries (EFCI), priced publication (www.feni.be).

15 http://www.union-network.org/UNIPROPERTYN.nsf/2aca427bf4dd1055c125719c004b7986/$FILE/DaytimeCleaningDeclaration.pdf

16 http://www.union-network.org/UNIPROPERTYN.nsf/2aca427bf4dd1055c125719c004b7986/$FILE/DaytimeCleaningDeclaration.pdf

an objective system of quality criteria, which could be established using the procurement guide [17].

- A health and safety training manual [18] which lists all risks and risk factors in the sector, namely: slips, trips and falls, manual handling and working postures, dangerous products, electrical hazards, work equipment, working environment, violence, stress and work organisation. The manual also describes preventive measures that should be taken by managers and supervisors and the workers themselves.
- A manual on musculoskeletal disorders entitled 'Ergonomics in cleaning operations' which tackles the ergonomic aspects of common cleaning tasks (looking at issues such as working postures) and links to safety issues to further reduce the risk of occupational accidents in the cleaning sector.
- 'Industrial cleaning — European training kit for office cleaning' — a training manual and booklets dedicated to giving workers the professional skills required for common office cleaning tasks [19].

European health and safety research on cleaning 2.4.

2.4.1. BIOMED

A large European project on cleaning was conducted from 1996 to 1999 by several European institutes. It involved the industry and unions as well as government authorities. The project was funded by the European Commission (Biomedical and Health Research Programme — BIOMED 2) and the findings as well as the practical approaches and recommendations have influenced many activities on occupational health and safety in the sector.

The project was based on earlier activities such as a research project at the Heidelberg clinic in Hamburg [20], which produced valuable insights into health and safety problems faced by cleaning staff, and came about because of concerted efforts by important stakeholders such as doctors, workers' representatives and health insurers.

2.4.2. Risk in Cleaning

A four-year multidisciplinary research and development project entitled 'Risk in Cleaning — Prevention of Health and Safety Risks in Professional Cleaning and the Work Environment' was conducted by experts from Denmark, Germany, Italy and

17 UNI-Europa (Union Network International) and EFCI (European Federation of Cleaning Industries); Selecting best value — A guide for organisations awarding contracts for cleaning services (http://ec.europa.eu/employment_social/dsw/public/actRetrieveText.do?id=10242).

18 Lorenzo Munar Suard, Guy Lebeer, Health & safety in the office cleaning sector — European manual for employees, Centre de Sociologie de la Santé of the Université Libre de Bruxelles (ULB) and the Centre de Diffusion de la Culture Sanitaire a.s.b.l., project partners UNI-Europa and EFCI.

19 The materials can be requested online from the European Federation of Cleaning Industries (FENI) (http://www.feni.be).

20 See Huth, Elke, Krueger, Detlef, Zorzi, Gerlinde, Gesundheitsförderung im Krankenhausbetrieb — Funktionsbereich Reinigung, Abschlußbericht, Fachhochschule Hamburg, 1996.

Finland. Links were set up with specialists in Spain and the United Kingdom. The aim of the 'Risk in Cleaning' project was to investigate risks associated with cleaning in various EU countries, examining the role played by working conditions and individual characteristics of health problems. A parallel goal was to devise ways of mitigating and eradicating those risks.

The project partners realised[21] that since the 1980s the cleaning industry had been under intense pressure to improve productivity and save costs. However, less attention had been paid to health and safety issues and ergonomic aspects of cleaning, and there was no sound scientific knowledge on exposure and acute response and their causal relation to disorders. The project set out to identify and to assess all the significant risk factors in the workplace and environment including research into the connection between risk factors and the aetiology[22] of diseases as well as the control of risks. The project also evaluated various cleaning methods, tools, cleaning agents, work organisation, working hours, aetiologic histories, medical findings, the quality of cleaning, indoor climate and the environmental impacts.

Some of their findings are shown here.

- Musculoskeletal disorders are multi-causal with physical, psychosocial and personal risk factors. In Germany an orthopaedic control instrument was developed that allows doctors to identify critical conditions relatively quickly and to prescribe rehabilitation measures.
- Irritative hand eczema is common in cleaning work. The risk factors are wet work, the number and age of children at home, and genetic factors (atopic dermatitis). Skin symptoms seem to arise relatively quickly at the beginning of the employment period and they continue permanently or sporadically.
- The design of buildings, fittings and furniture, as well as cleaning tools, machines and methods is poor from the viewpoint of both ergonomics and productive and efficient cleaning. The risks related to psychosocial and physical work and the environment are common. Cleaners have little or no control over their work and few opportunities to develop their career. The cardiorespiratory and musculoskeletal load on cleaners is high, and it produces a considerable risk of overstrain among women with low capacity for manual work. Ergonomics is an essential element for the promotion of cleaners' efficiency, health and well-being[23].
- A broad spectrum of cleaning agents has been developed for various applications. There is a complex pattern of exposure to them and health problems, such as allergies and asthma, among cleaning personnel are reported.

Finally, the project developed preventive strategies. Participatory ergonomics seems to be feasible and effective in producing constant improvements in cleaning equipment, methods and organisation. Strategies take into account the work environment in cleaning and include:

- changes in work organisation (e.g. proposal on daytime cleaning);

21 See final project report: Krueger, Detlef, Louhevaara, Veikko, Nilsen, Jette, Schneider, Thomas (eds), 'Risk assessment and preventive strategies in cleaning work', Werkstattberichte aus Wissenschaft + Technik. Wb 13. Hamburg 1997. The project is also presented online (http://www.rzbd.fh-hamburg.de/~prbiomed/risk_assessment.html and http://www.ttl.fi/Internet/English/Information/Electronic+journals/Tyoterveiset+journal/1999-02+Special+Issue/06.htm).

22 The cause of a disease or abnormal condition.

23 See also for example, Ruseph Kumar Ergonomic Evaluation and Design of Tools in Cleaning Occupation 2006:16 ISSN 1402-1544 ISRN LTU DT 0616 SE and Kumar, R., Chaikumarn, M., Kumar, S., 2005b. Physiological, subjective and postural loads in passenger train wagon cleaning using a conventional and redesigned cleaning tool, International Journal of Industrial Ergonomics, 35, pp. 931–938.

- giving cleaners more opportunities to influence the organisation, pace and scheduling of their work, and to choose the equipment and team they are allocated to work with;
- giving cleaners opportunities for career advancement, professional perks and benefits as well as support from their immediate supervisors;
- making a special effort to reduce repetitive and strenuous arm movements and poor working postures;
- sufficient education and training (e.g. courses on how to work with mops);
- development and evaluation of utensils and methods (e.g. appropriate handles);
- changing to less harmful cleaning fluids and less wet work;
- suggestions on building construction;
- giving cleaners more recognition for the valuable service they provide, and making a greater effort to improve their health, efficiency and productivity; cleaning should be appreciated as a job that requires specialised expertise and its organisation and ergonomic aspects need to be taken seriously and planned carefully.

The project has assisted ongoing initiatives and many of its ideas and recommendations have been taken forward in other projects and activities, such as joint efforts between manufacturers and cleaners to develop new, more user-friendly equipment, an ergonomic approach to the training of cleaners (Moving with Awareness), continued efforts to propagate dry and damp cleaning methods, team-based cleaning, job enrichment, consideration of cleaning aspects in the design of hotel rooms, etc.

2.5. EUROCITIES' CARPE PROCUREMENT GUIDE

2.5.1. Introduction

EUROCITIES was founded in 1986 as a network which brings together the local governments of more than 130 large cities in over 30 European countries. EUROCITIES provides a platform for its member cities to share knowledge and ideas, to exchange experiences, to analyse common problems and develop solutions, through a wide range of forums, working groups, projects, activities and events [24].

The network developed the CARPE (cities as responsible purchasers in Europe) procurement guide, propagating responsible procurement, which they define as aiming 'at integrating social, environmental, and/or ethical concerns into public purchasing decisions' [25]. The guide can be applied to almost all types of purchases by local authorities where cleaning services are explicitly mentioned. The guide proposes a variety of possible criteria and related award methods. Applying the guide, authorities would have to select those criteria they think would best suit their

24 http://www.eurocities.org

25 Moschitz S., CARPE guide to responsible procurement, EUROCITIES Secretariat, Brussels, 2005, 2nd edn, p. 6. Available as a pdf (http://www.european-fair-trade-association.org/FairProcura/Doc/Brochures/CARPE_guide_to_responsible_procurement_secondedition.pdf).

needs and then define their specific awarding method. The guide also refers to the appropriate World Trade Organisation (WTO) rules and the European legislation.

2.5.2. Aims and objectives

The EUROCITIES network provides advice and offers resources for public purchasers, in the form of guidelines and information. The aim is to change the public procurement field by persuading professionals that good purchasing also means environmentally, socially and ethically sound purchasing.

2.5.3. Scope of the project — what was done

The general approach is to influence service and product providers by specifying procurement criteria, to get greener, more social and ethical services and products for European cities. In explaining what is meant by 'integrating social concerns' into the procurement process the document highlights the promotion of employment, equal opportunities, and accessibility, the safeguarding of working conditions, and the support of the social economy [26].

The CARPE guide notes that 'National legislation on employment, social security, health and safety as well as collective agreements protects employees in areas including fair pay, workers rights, and healthy and safe workplaces and must be applied during delivery of a public contract.' The guide recognises that contracts being awarded on the basis of lowest price bid can lead to a loss of quality of service and a risk of (occupational safety and health) legislation being breached. Taking quality into account in procurement along with explicit demands for legal compliance can ensure that public contracts are carried out according to law and to high quality standards.

Procurement experiences of the City of Stockholm using CARPE

From 2002, Stockholm used the CARPE guide to combat underground labour in the construction sector and has also expanded these contract clauses to the cleaning sector. This has been done in cooperation with the trade unions, whose assistance is particularly useful in monitoring compliance. The detailed guide developed by EUROCITIES provided a solid basis to further develop the specific criteria in Stockholm.

To be considered for a contract, a company had to present documents certifying its fulfilment of tax and social security obligations. The company's compliance with social security, tax and wage obligations could then be checked by the public administration during the contract period. Additionally, in some cases, a contract performance condition stipulated that workers have to carry ID badges which the city can compare to the official list of staff which the contactor is obliged to supply. The monitoring could be done by the procurement department or by an external consultant.

Stockholm used this instrument to enforce equal opportunities on public contracts. The clause allowed the city to cancel a contract if a company did not adhere to anti-discrimination legislation during the contract period. Before taking such radical measures, however, the city tried to solve the problem with the company. The modified clause also gave the right, at any time of contract

26 Ibid, p. 20.

delivery, to demand a written explanation from the companies on how they were fulfilling their anti-discrimination legal obligations.

In Stockholm there was a long political struggle on the question of whether procurement is a suitable tool to prevent underground labour, or whether it should be left to the competent authority (tax authorities, prosecution office, or police). There were also doubts on how the clause would be followed up, as there is a lack of structures and staff for checking all contracts. Checking whether large contractors conform to anti-discrimination legislation should not be that difficult, but considerable resources are needed to follow up on all suppliers of goods.

Due to these problems it was decided, in 2007, not to continue the projects. However the criteria are still in use in some of the city's construction contracts and the trade unions do fulfil their part of the deal. The criteria are also used in at least one contract for cleaning services. Regarding the enforcement of equal opportunities, the executive office has a commission to write a new clause with a slightly changed content, but, on the whole, the clause is still used in all contracts, although no example is known of a contract being cancelled because of a breach of the clause.

Further information may be obtained from
Silke Moschitz
CARPE Project Coordinator
EUROCITIES Secretariat
Square de Meeus 18, 1050 Brussels, BELGIUM
Tel. +32 25520876
E-mail: s.moschitz@eurocities.be
Maria Laxvic, City of Stockholm
E-mail: maria.laxvik@stadshuset.stockholm.se
Jacob Krokstedt, Stockholm Procurement Strategist
E-mail: jacob.krokstedt@stadshuset.stockholm.se

2.6. The Social Platform procurement campaign: 'Making the most of public money'

The Social Platform is an association of over 30 European non-governmental organisations, federations and networks in the social sector, including the European Disability Forum (EDF), the European Federation of Public Service Unions (EPSU), the British trade union GMB, the European Confederation of Workers' Cooperatives, Social Cooperatives and Participative Enterprises (CECOP), the European Trade Union Confederation (ETUC), EUROCITIES and the European Environmental Bureau (EEB).

In 2004 the platform launched the campaign 'Making the most of public money' at Member State level to urge governments and public authorities to include social, ethical and environmental considerations in public procurement processes to use the new European legislation providing more opportunities in this field[27]. The campaigners asked the public to send a model letter to their governments listing practical possibilities and asking authorities to make use of them. A guideline with the same title was developed[28] calling on national governments to take action on public procurement. Cleaners were an important target group of this campaign.

2.7. European standard EN13549: 2001 cleaning services

This European standard offers a guideline for the procurement of cleaning services and allows bids to be selected objectively by applying standardised output criteria. While occupational safety and health is not mentioned as a specific criterion, the standard has a direct influence on cleaners' workload.

The Committee on Standardisation, CEN, concluded in 2005: 'taking into account the size of the cleaning industry, further European standards are needed. It is estimated by EFCI (European Federation of Cleaning Industries) that, in 1997, public authorities in six European countries alone contracted out the equivalent of EUR 5.8 billion of industrial cleaning services ... European standards on the qualification of personnel, on code of practice or contract drafting could be further developed at the European level'[29].

At an international level, a new ISO committee on requirements and recommendations for cleaning services has been formed as a result of a German initiative. On 29 March 2007, experts from Europe and Asia gathered in Berlin for the inaugural meeting of ISO/PC 233. The ISO standard under development will serve as a reference for calls for tenders, give guidance on the form tenders are to take, and facilitate their evaluation. This could be especially useful in global calls for tenders.

The project is part of a series of specific and complex ISO projects that take account of the growing internationalisation of services, with Germany holding the convenorship and DIN, the German standards institute, the secretariat for this particular project[30].

27 http://www.socialplatform.org/Policy.asp?DocID=8268

28 Available online (http://www.socialplatform.org/News.asp?news=9521), the guide refers also to the SDC procurement guide: Selecting best value — A guide for organisations awarding contracts for cleaning services, see Selecting best value — A guide for organisations awarding contracts for cleaning services (http://ec.europa.eu/employment_social/dsw/public/actRetrieveText.do?id=10242).

29 CEN, 'Final Report on European Commission Programming Mandate M/340 in the Field of Services' (http://www.cen.eu/cenorm/businessdomains/businessdomains/services/finalreportm340.pdf).

30 http://www.din.de/cmd;jsessionid=2AB2C6860D8D6F7EF6BBD546E82FF120.3?menuid=49589&contextid=din&cmstextid=57840&cmsareaid=49589&cmsrubid=56731&2=&menurubricid=56731-&level=tpl-artikel&languageid=en

Actions by the ILO 2.8.

The International Labour Organisation (ILO) seeks to ensure that labour standards are respected through conventions, which are legally binding international treaties that may be ratified by Member States, or recommendations, which serve as non-binding guidelines. International labour standards are backed by a supervisory system that is unique at the international level and helps to ensure that countries implement the conventions they ratify. The ILO regularly examines the application of standards in Member States and points out areas where they could be better applied. In addition, the ILO produces Codes of Practice [31] that are non-legally binding, practical recommendations intended to supplement the provision of national laws and standards. Many conventions, recommendations [32], and codes of practice relate to issues that affect cleaning workers. A list of some of them can be found in the annexes to this report.

In addition to these approaches, the ILO International Occupational Safety and Health Information Centre (CIS) provides information to prevent occupational injuries and diseases. CIS produces International Hazard Datasheets that list, in a standard format, various hazards to which workers may be exposed in the course of their normal work. They are a source of information rather than advice.

A datasheet is available for cleaners [33]. To give an example of the information provided, under the heading 'Ergonomic, psychosocial and organisational factors' it notes that one issue is 'psychological stress due to dissatisfaction at work as a result of alleged low social status, boredom, monotony, low salary, problematic personal relations with peers and/or superiors', and goes on to say 'these ergonomic and psychosocial problems may be especially severe in the case of female cleaners, who in some countries constitute a large proportion of workers engaged in this occupation'.

The datasheet is intended to be a source of information about the causes of occupational accidents and illnesses to help the relevant professionals to devise and implement proper means of prevention.

2.8.1. Application of the international hazard datasheet for industrial cleaners in Poland

Poland's Centralny Instytut Ochrony Pracy — Państwowy Instytut Badawczy (Central Institute for Labour Protection — National Research Institute [34]), or CIOP-PIB is just one institute that uses an adapted version of this datasheet.

31 http://www.ilo.org/public/english/protection/safework/cops/english/index.htm

32 See ILO database of conventions and recommendations (http://www.ilo.org/ilolex/english/index.htm).

33 http://www.ilo.org/public/english/protection/safework/cis/products/hdo/htm/cleaner.htm

34 http://www.ciop.pl

The four-page datasheets contain the following information:

- page 1: information on the most frequent hazards associated with a defined profession;
- page 2: details of characteristics and side effects associated with agents encountered in the job, occasionally supplemented with suggestions concerning prevention of their adverse effects;
- page 3: recommendations concerning actions and preventive measures for chosen hazards;
- page 4: information for safety and health professionals in the environment.

Knowledge about the causes of accidents and illnesses helps in devising and implementing proper prevention methods. For industrial cleaners, risk factors include:

- cleaners often work with or near moving machinery, conveyors or vehicles which may cause injuries;
- floors are often damp and slippery during cleaning, which may cause injuries resulting from falling, stumbling or slipping;
- cleaners make extensive use of chemical substances that may cause irritation to the skin, eye irritation as well as irritations of the nasal and throat mucous membranes;
- cleaners' work often requires considerable physical effort; the job is often done in an unnatural posture and requires repetitive motions that may cause pain.

The following table shows an extract from the hazard datasheet for industrial cleaners.

Table 1: Workplace environment factors associated with working as a cleaner and their possible influence on health

Workplace environment factors associated with working as a cleaner and their possible influence on health	
 Factors likely to cause accidents	• Ladders, possibility of an injury resulting from falling from height • Slippery and uneven surfaces — a possibility of injuries caused by falling, slipping or stumbling • Sharp tools, scrap metal, broken glass — a possibility of injuries caused by a prick, cut or puncture
 Physical agents	• Excessive noise from cleaning machines — a possibility of hearing impairment
 Chemical agents and dusts	• Chlorine in cleaning and washing preparations (usually sodium hypochlorite) — possibility of poisoning • Widely used chemical substances (solvents, cleaning, rinsing and disinfecting agents) may cause skin and eye irritations as well as irritations of nasal and throat mucous membranes
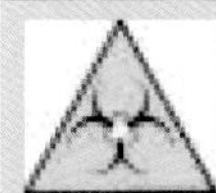 Biological agents	• Fungi allergens contained in dust — may cause allergies and pneumonia with asthmatic symptoms • Rodent excrement containing micro-organisms — possibility of infection with contagious diseases
 Ergonomic, psychosocial factors and factors associated with work organisation	Cleaners' work is associated with considerable physical effort; the job is often done in a forced posture (bending, kneeling) and often requires repetitive actions (e.g. swabbing floors) which may cause musculoskeletal disorders

South Australian risk assessment guidelines

Action to protect cleaners is happening around the world. The governmental South Australian Occupational Health and Safety agency operates the 'Safe Work' website. Among others they have published detailed 'SAFER task' checklists for cleaners [1]. These checklists are designed to help cleaning operators identify and assess common hazards associated with bathroom and toilet care, carpet cleaning, clinical waste, dusting, mopping, floor stripping, sweeping, vacuuming, violence and others. They recommend actions to minimise the risk of injury whilst performing the tasks.

1 http://www.safework.sa.gov.au/contentPages/docs/clean4OhsChecklists.pdf

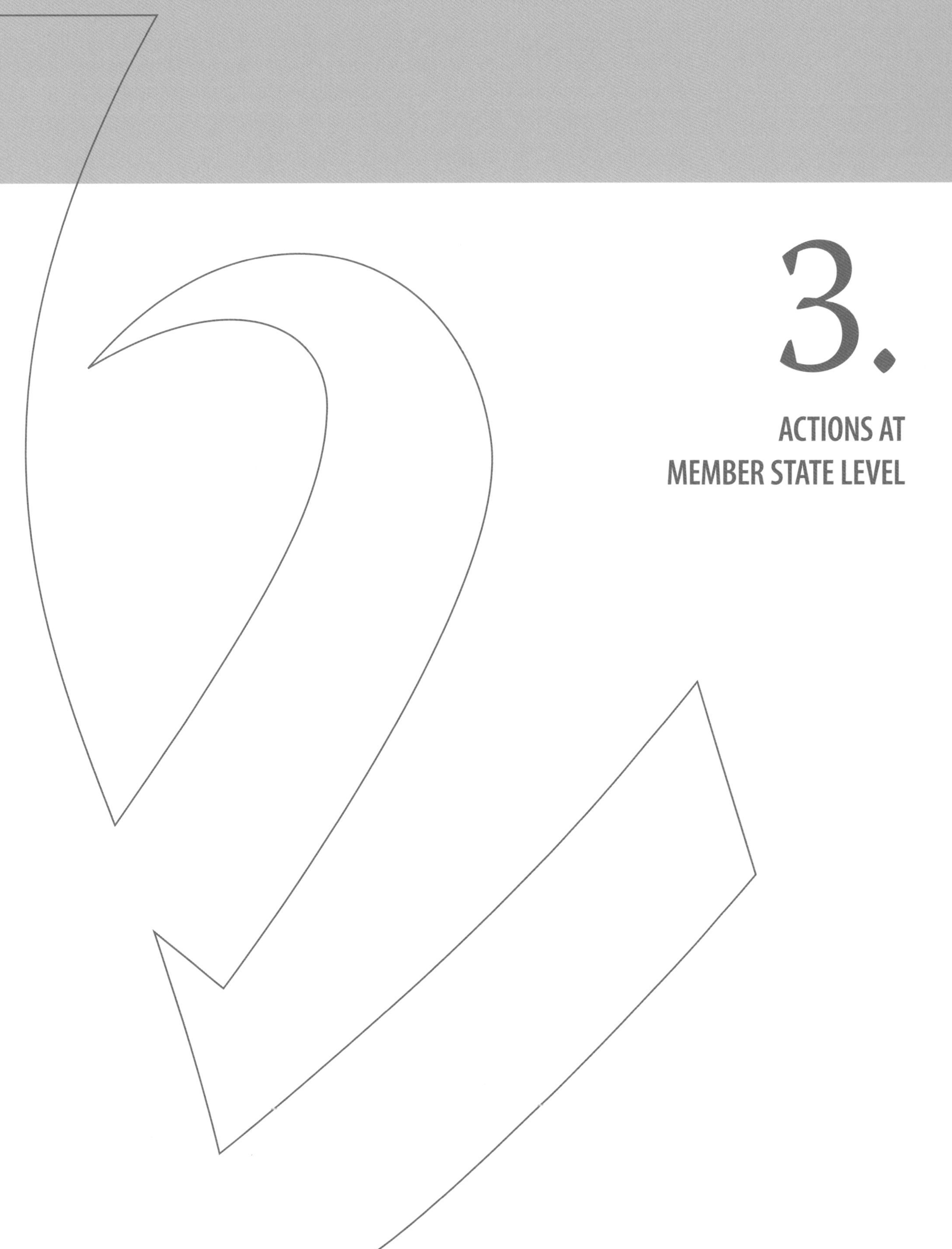

3.

ACTIONS AT MEMBER STATE LEVEL

Member States are taking a range of actions to improve the working conditions of cleaners. These actions are not always 'traditional' occupational safety and health approaches, as some of the challenges to cleaning workers stem from the particular demographic, economic, and social structure of the Member State in question. The actions described here vary from providing technical rules to tripartite initiatives, training programmes to exhibitions. Several may overlap with the workplace-focused initiatives described in the next chapter. These actions are intended to illustrate the range of initiatives that are being taken and can be used to take a broad approach to reducing the risks to cleaning workers.

3.1. Déparis in the cleaning sector — a participatory guide for screening of risks (Belgium)

- Strategy for the management of occupational risks
- Participatory approach involves users
- Enables screening of risks in the cleaning sector

3.1.1. Introduction

The Sobane strategy is an instrument that helps avoid, resolve or decrease safety-related problems. Sponsored by the European Social Fund[35], and developed by the Federal Public Services Employment Labour and Social Dialogue in Belgium, the Sobane strategy consists of four different levels: **S**creening, **ob**servation, **an**alysis and **e**xpertise.

The four different levels: screening, observation, analysis and expertise will be realised spontaneously in most organisations. This procedure is often neither systematic nor efficient because of the lack of suitable instruments to perform screening and observations, and because the task is frequently passed to prevention advisors rather than carried out in collaboration with all the parties concerned, thereby taking advantage of their complementary knowledge.

The Sobane strategy therefore aims to provide screening and observation instruments for ordinary, non-specialised workers so that all relevant partners have input into the process. For each of the four levels solutions are needed to improve the working conditions. Research on the next level is only necessary if after the introduction of the improvements the situation is still unacceptable.

- At the screening stage, the main problems should be identified internally.
- During the observation level, those problems not solved at the earlier stages are examined in greater depth.

35 European Social Fund (http://ec.europa.eu/employment_social/esf/).

- If risks still remain, the analysis stage engages external prevention advisors to consider a problem.
- Finally, if there is a complex situation needing specific measures, the relevant experts are engaged.

Sobane provides the Déparis consultation guide to enable users to carry out the screening phase properly. This guide sets out all the steps that should be followed in screening and points out which sources of risk should be investigated.

3.1.2. Aims and objectives

The Déparis consultation guide enables workers to provide a detailed account of the state of affairs in their work situation, which they know better than anyone else. This guide puts the workers in the centre, not to give their opinion or answer questions, but to talk about practical details which make it possible for them to carry out their work in optimal conditions — for themselves as well as for the organisation.

3.1.3. Scope of the project — what was done

This guide lists all steps that should be followed to screen risks efficiently. One of the steps is to have a discussion about occupational risks and their possible solutions. The guide features 17 sections with sources of risks. For each section several topics have to be discussed to determine who does what and when. The sections are:

- Rooms and working areas
- Work organisation
- Occupational accidents
- Electrical risks and fire danger
- Work apparatus and visual signals (e.g. lights, screens)
- Materials, hand tools, machinery
- Working postures
- Manual effort and goods handling
- Lighting and noise
- Vibrations
- Air quality
- Thermal environmental factors
- Autonomy and individual responsibilities
- Content of the work
- Time pressure
- Industrial relations between workers and line management
- Psychosocial environment.

The final synthesis summarises the assessments from all 17 sections. An inventory contains the proposed improvements and concrete actions as well as the aspects that have to be further analysed in the observation phase.

Involved parties

The project was sponsored by the European Social Fund and the Federal Public Services Employment, Labour and Social Dialogue. The project involved experts

from the Catholic University of Liège), IDEWE[36], the external services for Prevention and Protection at work (PROVIKMO) and the prevention service for the construction sector (SEFMEP). The graphic support and the layout of the CD-ROM were done by the NTF department (Nouvelles Technologies et Formation) from CIFoP (Centre Interuniversitaire de Formation Permanente, Mr J.F. Husson).

Means/outputs

A CD-Rom and a brochure were produced within the framework of the project, and many printed guides are available to help implement the Sobane strategy.

Target group

The Sobane strategy in general is intended for use by prevention advisors, such as medical officers, safety officers and ergonomists, as well as chief executives who are responsible for company prevention policy, technical workers and workers' representatives, etc.

3.1.4. Transferability of the project

The Sobane strategy in general can be used for all sectors. The Déparis guide exists in two versions: the basic version, which can be used by all sectors, and subsidiary versions that are adapted to specific sectors, such as cleaning and construction.

Documents and information on the Sobane strategy are freely available online in Dutch, English, French, German, Portuguese and Spanish[37], making it accessible to stakeholders all over the world.

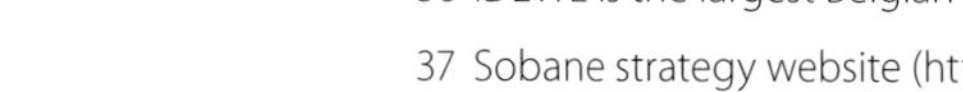

36 IDEWE is the largest Belgian occupational health service.

37 Sobane strategy website (http://www.sobane.be/).

3.1.5. Details of initiative

Table 2: Sobane: screening, observation, analysis, expertise; Déparis: dépistage participative des risques

Title	Sobane: screening, observation, analysis, expertise; Déparis: dépistage participative des risques
Type of project	Sobane: strategy for the management of occupational risks Déparis: participatory consultation guide as an instrument for the screening level in the Sobane strategy
Sector	All sectors
Lead organisation	Belgian Federal Public Services Labour, Employment and Social Dialogue
Sources	Sobane strategy en opsporingsgids Déparis, Federale overheidsdienst werkgelegenheid, arbeid en sociaal overleg, Januari 2007 http://www.sobane.be
Contact information	Website of the Sobane strategy http://www.sobane.be/ The brochure can be obtained freely via the Federal Public Services employment, labour and social dialogue, http://www.werk.belgie.be Cel Publicaties van de FOD Werkgelegenheid, Arbeid en Sociaal Overleg Ernest Blerotstraat 1, 1070 Brussels, BELGIUM Tel. +32 22334211, Fax +32 22334236 E-mail: publicaties@werk.belgie.be

3.2. Cooperation agreement against unlawful labour in the cleaning sector (Belgium)

- Cooperation between government, unions and employers' association
- Aim is to combat unlawful labour in cleaning sector

3.2.1. Introduction

As part of its policy to increase the employment rate, the Belgian government decided to intensify the fight against unlawful or unregulated labour, as illegal employment in Belgium is estimated to account for 10–20 % of gross domestic product.

On 1 March 2003 the Ministry of Employment, Labour and Social Consultation, the Belgian employers' association from the cleaning branch ABSU[38], the Christian trade union ACV and the trade union ABVV signed a cooperation agreement to combat unlawful labour in the cleaning sector[39].

38 ABSU is the umbrella organisation dealing with training countrywide; it also controls the Social Fund of the Belgian cleaning industry.

39 Federal Public Services Employment, Labour and Social Dialogue, Guide from A to Z, Battle against illegal labour on (http://www.werk.belgie.be/detailA_Z.aspx?id=932 - AutoAncher2), 'Zwartwerk en

An action plan was drawn up including several measures aimed at combating the practice; some focused on prevention and others on suppression. One of the preventive measures is to encourage the industries most affected to become more involved in the battle against illegal employment. Through close cooperation five agreements have been drawn up to combat the practice: two in the construction sector, one in the security sector, one in transportation and one in the cleaning sector.

These agreements are important because unregistered labour undermines the social security system in Belgium, thus threatening the solidarity between the employed and unemployed, young and older employees, healthy and sick people, people with an income and people without one, families with and without children, etc. But apart from the effect on the country's social security system, the battle against illegal labour is also important to protect the workers themselves. Performing 'grey' labour has some negative consequences when it comes to working conditions. As these workers have no legal employment contract with the employer they are not insured for occupational accidents.

Undeclared work leading to unsafe working conditions

A study by the Brussels Free University[1] confirmed that clandestine or undeclared employment can lead to unsafe and unhealthy working conditions. This study says that clandestine or undeclared employment is one of the main reasons for the fierce competition that exists in the cleaning sector. The study also explains how this competition influences the working conditions of cleaners.

This competition has obvious consequences for the health and safety of workers, all the more so since about 80 % (this figure can vary by State) of the costs invoiced to customers are made up of labour costs. One way, therefore, of reducing costs is to juggle with the 'labour' variable and this can have numerous consequences on the health of workers:

- high work rates;
- reducing the number of employees (fewer workers to do the same work);
- non-compliance with health and safety standards to reduce costs and be more competitive;
- more pressure on workers (stress, tiredness);
- workers do not have the resources (tools, products) to do their job in a way that is safe, professional, and dignified (problems of self-respect, pressure).

1 Centre de Sociologie de la Santé (Brussels Free University), Elaboration of a European training manual in the field of health and safety for workers in the cleaning sector, Sectoral study, UNI-Europa — FENI/EFCI, Directorate-General for Employment and Social Affairs, June 2000.

fraude: een bedreiging voor de welvaartstaat', Pierre-Paul Maeter (Chief of cabinet of Minister of employment Laurette Onkelinx) (http://socialsecurity.fgov.be/bib/aankondigingen/P-Maeter-orig-NL-aangep-gek.doc).

3.2.2. Aims and objectives

The purpose of the agreement is to send a signal to all stakeholders in the cleaning sector, give greater recognition to the cleaning profession, and to battle dishonest competition practices such as:

- using workers who are not legally resident in the European Union;
- 'grey' or unregulated labour;
- not complying with general and sectoral regulations;
- failing to carry out statutory registration procedures, and misleading clients about accreditation [40].

3.2.3. Scope of the project — what was done

The cooperation agreement against illicit forms of labour in the cleaning sector

On 1 March 2003 the Federal Public Services of employment, labour and social dialogue, the Belgian employers' association from the cleaning branch ABSU, the Christian trade union ACV and the trade union ABVV signed a cooperation agreement against 'underground' labour in the cleaning branch for a period of 18 months [41].

Responsibilities and involvement of all parties

The Federal Public Services employment, labour and social dialogue

The board of directors from the Federal Public Services were tasked with:

- making sure that contracts only are signed with approved cleaning companies that have acquired the 'cleaning quality label';
- inviting all other public services of the federal government, the districts and communities to apply the same rule;
- improving their cooperation with the legal authorities and labour inspectorates to enforce the rules;
- asking the Minister of employment to use his powers to stop illicit employment practices.

The inspection services

The inspection services were tasked with standardising and unifying their control measures to combat unlawful labour practices. The inspection services will report periodically on the investigations they performed in companies from the sector and the results of these investigations. This report will contain information on the type and frequency of violations.

The trade unions

The unions committed themselves not to negotiate any agreement that would enable avoidance of social security payments or minimum wage obligations. They also agreed to publicise all convictions resulting from violations.

40 Cooperation agreement published in ABSU — UGBN Memoclean 02/2003 (http://www.absugbn.be/pdffiles/CONVPAnl.pdf).

41 Cooperation agreement published in ABSU — UGBN Memoclean 02/2003 (http://www.absugbn.be/pdffiles/CONVPAnl.pdf).

ABSU

The ABSU pledged to cooperate with the inspection services, provide workable and reliable control measures, and publicise any convictions resulting from violation of these rules. Additionally, the ABSU will withhold or remove the 'cleaning quality label' from any company that uses dishonest competition practices, including:

- employing workers who are not legally resident in Europe;
- using 'grey' labour;
- failing to comply with general and sector-related regulations;
- using irregular or unlawful contracts.

3.2.4. Evaluation and transferability of the project

Annual reports have been drawn up giving an overview of investigations carried out, the observed violations, the number of workers who have been regularised, etc.

The transferability of these kinds of agreements has been proved because already four other agreements have been concluded: two in the construction sector, one in the security sector and one in the personal transportation sector.

3.2.5. Details of initiative

Table 3: Cooperation agreement against unlawful labour in the cleaning sector

Title	Cooperation agreement against unlawful labour in the cleaning sector
Type of project	Cooperation agreement between the government, employers associations and trade unions
Sector	Cleaning
Others involved	Employers association ABSU http://www.absugbn.be Trade Union ABVV http://www.abvv.be and http://www.accg.be Trade Union ACV http://www.acv-online.be and http://acv-voeding-diensten.acv-online.be/
Date of project	1 March 2003 for 18 months
Information sources	Federal Public Services Employment, Labour and Social Dialogue, Guide from A to Z, Battle against the illegal labour http://www.werk.belgie.be/detailA_Z.aspx?id=932#AutoAncher2 'Zwartwerk en fraude: een bedreiging voor de welvaartstaat', Pierre-Paul Maeter (Chief of cabinet of Minister of employment Laurette Onkelinx) http://socialsecurity.fgov.be/bib/aankondigingen/P-Maeter-orig-NL-aangep-gek.doc Cooperation agreement published in ABSU — UGBN Memoclean 02/2003 http://www.absugbn.be/pdffiles/CONVPAnl.pdf
Contact information	Federal Public Service Employment, Labour and Social dialogue http://www.meta.fgov.be/ Battle against illegal labour http://www.werk.belgie.be/detailA_Z.aspx?id=932

Battling against gender discrimination (Belgium)

Gender inequality is entrenched in the Belgian cleaning sector, so the social partners provided an education plan for women to improve their career prospects. In the sector, 35 % of employees work less than four hours a day and earn less than EUR 680 a month. Most of these employees are women: 43.5 % of females in the sector work in these conditions compared with 17.08 % of men. Centrale Culturelle Bruxelloise [1] and the trade union ABVV [2] set up a joint two-year project in 2005 to find a way to eliminate this inequality.

Investigations were carried out in dialogue with both female and male representatives and officials from the cleaning sector, to:

- identify the inequalities faced by female and male workers;
- acquire an insight into how work is divided between men and women in the cleaning sector;
- determine ways of removing the obstacles that hinder the promotion of women.

On the basis of these investigations, an education plan was drawn up to assist women in advancing in the cleaning sector, and to overcome the discrimination they face. Courses were made available in both Dutch and French [3].

1 Centrale Culturelle Bruxelloise vzw (http://www.fgtbbruxelles.be/Code/fr/c01_0007.htm).

2 ABVV Brussels (http://www.accg.be).

3 Further information can be found online: Een veelbelovend proefproject in de schoonmaaksector, ECHO-ABVV, March 2007 (http://www.fgtbbruxelles.irisnet.be/site/nl/denieuwewerker/Files/DeNW230207/).

Research on stress in the cleaning sector (Belgium) 3.3.

- Investigation of stress in the cleaning branch
- Causes and preventive measures identified
- Action manual compiled to combat stress

3.3.1. Introduction

The Belgian workforce is regularly confronted with work-related stress. Stress undermines the health of workers and has an influence on the absenteeism rate and the number of occupational accidents and diseases. The law obliges companies to have in place a policy concerning stress and to reduce its incidence where possible.

The social partners from the cleaning sector therefore decided to carry out a study on this topic with help from ABSU[42]. The results of the study enabled them to produce a manual on the subject of stress.

The training centre at ABSU and ULB performed a study on stress in the cleaning sector, which resulted in a brochure *De oorzaken van stress in de schoonmaak — een handboek voor actie* (The causes of stress in the cleaning sector — a manual for action).

3.3.2. Aims and objectives

The purpose of the research study was to help stakeholders in the sector fully understand the concept of stress and its causes and to make them aware of prevention measures. Building on this research, it was intended to prepare a manual containing advice, suggestions and recommendations to improve the work environment and tackle stress[43].

3.3.3. Scope of the project — what was done

Methodology

The study concerned the different sub-sectors of the cleaning sector such as internal and external traditional cleaning, industrial cleaning and refuse removal. A qualitative methodology was chosen for the research study. In addition to interviews held with representatives of unions and employers' associations, semi-structured conversations were held with key actors on an individual and collective basis. This methodology was chosen for several reasons.

- The researchers wanted to study the way workers experience stress: how they live with it, how they deal with it, how they talk about it, etc. It was considered important for workers to be able to apply the information in the manual to their own work situation.
- The researchers needed information from the workers themselves to ensure that the manual was based on actual situations.
- Many immigrants work in the cleaning sector; they are not always proficient in written Dutch so it was more appropriate to conduct verbal interviews rather than questionnaires.
- Questionnaires are based on certain stress concepts, which the researchers believed to be too narrow. Measuring stress leads to a focus on scores and too little emphasis on the causes and prevention measures[44].

The manual

The manual provides information about stress which can be used in the cleaning sector to analyse the causes of stress and take preventive measures.

The manual is in four parts:

- definition of stress at work;

42 Munar Suard L. et al., 2003.

43 Ibid.

44 Source: Munar Suard L. et al., 2003 & Opleidingscentrum van de schoonmaak, 2003.

- the second part presents the characteristics of the cleaning sector which are important to understand the causes of stress in the sector;
- the third part provides information about the legal obligations concerning stress at work that every employer has to fulfil and it also explains fundamental principles of stress prevention at work;
- the final part discusses the systematic analysis of the causes of stress and suggests some adapted preventive measures.

The manual also provides an inventory that can be used by employers to check whether the various stress risks are present in the organisation and to what extent. This enables employers to select and prioritise preventive measures.

3.3.4. Results and evaluation of the project

Since June 2006 health and safety committees in the workplace have been required to use the manual in their assessments. Feedback on the project indicated that the social partners believed that some sections of the manual need more detailed study and a sectoral approach, with a greater emphasis on the flexibility of the work, the pace of work (rate, speed), and the achievement of a work-life balance. Follow-up studies will be conducted.

3.3.5. Success factors

This manual can help employers take steps to prevent the development of high stress levels among their workers. It provides a useful inventory that can help employers set priorities among the different preventive measures that have to be taken to tackle the causes of stress in their organisation.

3.3.6. Details of initiative

Table 4: The causes of stress in the cleaning sector, a manual for action

Title	The causes of stress in the cleaning sector, a manual for action
Type of project	Research study that led to a practical manual
Sector	Cleaning
Lead organisation	Centre de Sociologie de la Santé, Université Libre de Bruxelles CSS (Sociology of health Centre, Free University of Brussels) Training centre of the cleaning sector
Others involved	Euroclean, General Office Maintenance (GOM), International Service System (ISS) and Watco (four cleaning organisations that were involved in the project)
Sources of information	Catherine Kestelyn, ABVV, reply on questions by mail, 8 August 2007 *De oorzaken van stress in de schoonmaak, Een handboek voor actie,* Opleidingscentrum van de schoonmaak, Augustus 2003 Munar Suard L. et al, *De oorzaken van stress in de schoonmaaksector,* January 2003, 121 pp. Staatsbladclip http://www.staatsbladclip
Contact information	Centre de Sociologie de la Santé, Université Libre de Bruxelles CSS (Sociology of Health Centre, Free University of Brussels) Avenue Jeanne 44, 1050 Brussels, BELGIUM Tel. +32 26503429 Opleidingscentrum van de schoonmaak v.z.w. (Training centre of the cleaning sector OCS) Nerviërslaan 117, bus 48 bis, 1040 Brussels, BELGIUM Tel. +32 27321342

Campaign: European Week for Safety and Health at Work 2007 (EU-OSHA)

Campaign: EU-OSHA — European Agency for Safety and Health at Work Lighten the Load — 22–26 October 2007

Czech Association of Cleaning — CAC (Czech Republic) 3.4.

- The Czech Association of Cleaning was founded to help members acquire professional knowledge — CAC also provides quality certification as proof of this knowledge

3.4.1. Introduction

Knowledge of occupational safety and the working environment is especially important in cleaning work. Chemical and biological agents in some detergents can pose a health risk, for example. Cleaning workers should have the knowledge to clean to a high standard without damaging the objects being cleaned, the environment, or harming other workers.

The Czech Association of Cleaning (CAC) was founded in 1998 as a non-profit organisation. Its members include companies and individuals involved in the cleaning industry and related activities.

3.4.2. Aims and objectives

The Czech Association of Cleaning aims to help its members gain professional knowledge and provide proof of this to the public by granting cleaning quality certification.

3.4.3. Scope of the project — what was done

The CAC and the Czech Society for Quality (CSQ)[45] jointly created a three-level certification system for the cleaning industry. The first level — basic — certification is the Cleaning Operator certificate, the subsequent step is the Cleaning Manager certificate and the highest level of certification is the Cleaning Specialist certificate.

The knowledge required for these certifications is specified in the standards ČSJ–CE – 128,129,138. It concerns various levels of knowledge including:

- safety at work and labour code; cleaning — identification of individual ideas, maintenance of values and role of workers;
- organisation of principles and processes;
- quality management — creation of the policy, management and control, verification by the management;
- quality improvement techniques — specification of the investigation technique, motivation, implementation of techniques, evaluation, benchmarking; economics; purchasing and supplier contracts;
- quality in logistics;
- cleaning and guarantees;

45 http://www.csq.cz

- social aspects;
- legal and regulatory aspects.

The Cleaning Operator certification test consists of a written exam with 25 questions, like a learner driver's test, and one oral question where three basic attributes are evaluated for five points each. The Cleaning Manager certification is done in three phases. The first part is a written test with 15 questions, then there is one oral question which is evaluated for three points and finally the applicant has to carry out a cleaning study for a chosen building. The highest level of the certification is the Cleaning Specialist, who is required to present a project on a selected building and answer oral questions related to it.

3.4.4. Results and evaluation of the project

- Development and distribution of flexible education material.
- More systematic and comprehensive delivery of training.
- Cooperation between cleaners and the teaching staff.
- Increased availability of safety and health information for cleaners.

3.4.5. Details of initiative

Table 5: CAC

Title	Česká asociace úklidů a čištění — CAC (Czech Association of Cleaning)
Type of project	Federation
Sector	Information
Lead organisation	Public Employment Services
Others involved	Irena Bartoňová Pálková, Head Federation, Novodvorská 1010/14, 142 01 Prague 4, Czech Republic Tel./Fax +42 261341911 E-mail: sekretariat@cac-clean.cz
Date of project	1998
Further information	Česká asociace úklidů a čištění http://www.uklid.to/default_en.asp

Procurement of cleaning agents — IKA (Denmark) 3.5.

- Helping purchasers in the procurement of cleaning agents
- Encouraging suppliers to develop safe cleaning agents

3.5.1. Introduction

This case study describes an example of guidelines used to define requirements in tenders for the procurement of cleaning agents. A working group appointed by the Foreningen af Offentlige Indkøbere — IKA (Association of Public Purchasers in Denmark) produced the guidelines. This working group comprised three people representing public purchasers, three suppliers and one representative of the Association of Danish Manufacturers and Importers of Soap, Detergents, Perfume, Cosmetics and Chemical Technical Products (SPT). As part of the development process, the guidelines were discussed with representatives from the Danish Working Environment Authority.

3.5.2. Aims and objectives

The IKA publication includes guidelines for use in tenders for the procurement of cleaning agents. The purpose of the guidelines is to:

- help purchasers ensure that all relevant requirements for the delivery of cleaning agents are included when tenders are prepared;
- encourage suppliers to develop more environmentally and occupationally safe cleaning agents;
- save purchasers time when preparing tenders by offering a fill-in template for the tender;
- save purchasers time when evaluating tenders by asking the tenderers standardised questions;
- save time for the suppliers of cleaning agents by ensuring standardised requirements from more purchasers.

3.5.3. Scope of the project — what was done

The guidelines include requirements relevant for the safety and health of both the cleaning staff and the environment. The requirements are ranked with regard to price, function, environmental impact and occupational safety and health aspects. On occupational safety and health grounds, the cleaning agents may not:

- be marketed in the form of powder or aerosol spray;
- contain dangerous substances, in keeping with Danish labelling criteria;
- contain specific detergents and complex binders;
- contain substances listed by the Danish Working Environment Authority as carcinogenic, harmful for reproduction, allergenic or neurotoxic;

- in general contain perfume, colours and product stabilisers.

The tenderers are asked to provide information on all ingredients of the cleaning agents to the Danish Occupational Health Service Centre to ensure that the cleaning agents fulfil the requirements. Suppliers are sometimes asked to provide samples of their products for testing purposes.

3.5.4. Results and evaluation of the project

Use of the guidelines

The guidelines were originally developed in 1996 and have been revised several times since. The guidelines are presently used only in Denmark as they are available only in Danish and are protected by copyright, but IKA is considering translating them into English. The guidelines are used primarily by purchasers in public institutions when purchasing chemicals for the cleaning of public offices and institutions such as schools, hospitals, etc. The developers estimate that up to February 2000 the guidelines had been used for approximately 75 tenders prepared by municipalities and 12 tenders prepared by counties. The guidelines and the requirements are also available in electronic format. The material, comprising 22 A4 pages, including appendices, is designed as a fill-in template and the tenderers can prepare their bids directly.

Effects of the guidelines

The IKA working group has determined that use of the guidelines has resulted in:

- product development of safer cleaning agents;
- less decentralised procurement in public institutions and therefore greater certainty that cleaning agents fulfil the outlined requirements;
- less time spent preparing and evaluating tenders.

The purchasers stress that they have saved time by following the guidelines, especially when preparing tender materials.

A representative from an Occupational Health Service Centre who has evaluated the guidelines believes that they have:

- forced suppliers to consider whether their cleaning agents fulfil the requirements and hence focused attention on the environmental impact of cleaning agents and their effects on occupational safety and health;
- increased use of cleaning agents from 'green' product lines;
- motivated suppliers to provide information about product ingredients;
- standardised the way information is provided by suppliers and so made OHS assessment more efficient.

Cleaners have also mainly reacted positively to the guidelines. When detergents and cleaning agents are purchased with a focus on the safety and health of the cleaning staff, they can have greater confidence in the job. It is difficult to say whether the working environment has been improved because of the requirements set up in the purchasing situation. It is therefore difficult for the individual cleaner to see a direct relationship between the 'new' cleaning agents and a better working environment. If, for example, a cleaner does not suffer from allergy and is not easily sensitised, the fact that the 'new' cleaning agents do not contain allergens will not automatically be recognised as an improvement. Only in the longer term, statistics may show that

fewer cleaners become allergic to cleaning agents. A few purchasers have also been asked about their experiences using the guidelines. Their responses indicate that they are satisfied with the guidelines and they stress that using them has helped them save time, especially when preparing tender material, because the guidelines include relevant requirements to be forwarded to the accepted tenderers.

3.5.5. Effectiveness

The guidelines seem to have helped focus more attention on the impact of cleaning agents on the safety and health of the cleaning staff. The guidelines help the tenderer to include appropriate requirements for the cleaning agents in terms of environmental impact and occupational safety and health. In the long term the standardised requirements will encourage manufacturers to develop more cleaning agents that fulfil the safety requirements. The guidelines are considered to be particularly applicable for large companies preparing tenders for the procurement of all kind of cleaning agents and public institutions, e.g. offices, schools, hospitals, etc.

3.5.6. Problems faced

When the guidelines were developed, the suppliers were represented by their trade organisation SPT. SPT was a little reluctant at first because it felt the criteria might be difficult for some of its member companies to fulfil. The project was postponed and more time allowed for product development, with the result that SPT now has a positive attitude to the guidelines. SPT includes information about the guidelines in its training courses for suppliers.

3.5.7. Details of initiative

Table 6: IKA — Procurement of cleaning agents

Title	IKA — Procurement of cleaning agents
Type of project	Establishing guidelines for procurement of cleaning agents
Lead organisation	IKA, Association of Public Purchasers in Denmark — IKA, Foreningen af Offentlige Indkøbere http://www.ika.holstebro.dk
Contact information	Foreningen af Offentlige Indkøbere — IKA (Association of Public Purchasers in Denmark) http://www.ika.holstebro.dk

Bar Service: a web tool for the cleaning sector (Denmark)

Branchearbejdsmiljørådet for service og tjenesteydelser (Bar Service)[1] is a forum where employers' associations and employee unions work together to improve the working environment. The forum makes available a great deal of useful information and tools for various economic sectors, including the cleaning sector. Some of the Danish language resources are listed here.

- Cleaning and work environment in pictures[2] (2005) — a guide for cleaners covering topics such as cleaning agents, PPE, and ergonomics.
- Instructions for ergonomic cleaning[3] (2004) — Cleaning and ergonomics — guideline for cleaning workers.
- Good practice for small cleaning companies[4] (2003) — important information for safety inspectors and employers.
- Use of cleaning products[5] (2001) — the guide provides information about cleaning agents, possible hazards they pose and safety and prevention measures; the target audience is cleaners.
- 10 tips for cleaning[6] (2003) — The most important things a cleaner has to know.
- Directory for cleaning workers in offices, schools, childcare and day-care facilities[7] (2000) — for safety inspectors.

1 Branchearbejdsmiljørådet for service og tjenesteydelser (forkortes BAR service og tjenesteydelser) (http://www.bar-service.dk).

2 http://www.bar-service.dk/Files/Billeder/BARservice/pdf/Rengoering%20vaskerier%20og%20renserier/reng+arbjsm_d_endelig_version.pdf

3 http://www.bar-service.dk/Files/Billeder/BARservice/pdf/Rengoering%20vaskerier%20og%20renserier/genpt_reng_ergo_a5_5_udgave.pdf

4 http://www.bar-service.dk/Files/Billeder/BARservice/pdf/Rengoering%20vaskerier%20og%20renserier/god_praksis_i_mindre_rengringsvirk.pdf

5 http://www.bar-service.dk/Files/Billeder/BARservice/pdf/Rengoering%20vaskerier%20og%20renserier/Vejledning_om_rengringsmidler.pdf

6 Available online (http://www.bar-service.dk/Files/Billeder/BARservice/pdf/Rengoering%20vaskerier%20og%20renserier/10_gode_rd_vejledning.pdf) and a poster is also available (http://www.bar-service.dk/Files/Billeder/BARservice/pdf/Rengoering%20vaskerier%20og%20renserier/10_gode_rd_plakat.pdf).

7 http://www.bar-service.dk/Files/Billeder/BARservice/pdf/Rengoering%20vaskerier%20og%20renserier/Kontorer.pdf

BGI Guides on safe cleaning (Germany) 3.6.

3.6.1. Introduction

The German Berufsgenossenschafen (institutions for statutory accident insurance and prevention) produce a number of guides relevant to cleaning.

- BGI[46] 659: Cleaning of premises and buildings
- BGI 5034: Cleaning of passenger trains
- BGI 835: Wash plant for interior cleaning of railway vehicles — Installation and Technical Equipment

3.6.2. BGI 659: Cleaning of premises and buildings

The Berufsgenossenschaft der Bauwirtschaft — BG BAU (Institute for Statutory Accident Insurance and Prevention for the building industry) produced this document, which focuses on the various hazards and risks to which cleaners are exposed. Specific hazards are described and illustrated in modules, along with steps to be taken to tackle each hazard. All modules are regularly updated, with the latest version dating from 2007.

BGI 659 gives practical support and advice in a simple, user-friendly format. The risks associated with cleaning work depend on the type of core activity carried out by the company concerned (hazards may include falls from height, electrical equipment, ergonomics and chemical and biological agents). The guide helps identify specific hazards and/or risks, gives a brief overview of the necessary steps and preventative measures to take, and summarises all required precautions and protective measures.

3.6.3. BGI 5034: Cleaning of passenger trains

This guide was produced by the 'rail transport' expert committee of the BG BAHNEN[47]. Published in 2007, BGI 5034 covers all the potentially significant health and safety related risks faced by maintenance and cleaning staff when cleaning railway vehicles. The guideline focuses on the code of conduct to be adopted by cleaning staff to prevent and control the risks inherent in their work. A distinction is made between internal and external rail carriage cleaning. Additional risks covered are the hazards related to specific tasks carried out by the cleaning staff such as refilling of potable water tanks, toilet maintenance (emptying of waste tank), etc. The guide covers risk assessment, and provides a user's manual and information on various relevant topics, including first aid.

46 The I stands for 'information' in the document number.

47 Berufsgenossenschaft der Straßen-, U-Bahnen und Eisenbahnen — Institute for statutory accident insurance and prevention for tramways, underground and surface railways.

Table 7: Cleaning of premises and buildings, BGI 659

Title	Cleaning of premises and buildings, BGI 659
Type of project	Risk assessment and advice on cleaning premises and buildings; information on paper and the Internet
Sector	Insured workers and private contractors involved in the maintenance and cleaning of buildings
Lead organisation	Berufsgenossenschaft der Bauwirtschaft Landsberger Strasse 309 80687 Munich, GERMANY
Others involved	Expert committee 'Building' Expert committee 'Civil engineering'
Date of project	Last update 2007
Source of information	Website of Hauptverband der gewerblichen Berufsgenossenschaften (HVBG) in Kooperation mit dem Carl Heymanns Verlag http:// www.arbeitssicherheit.de Berufsgenossenschaft der Bauwirtschaft http://www.bgbau.de
Contact information	Berufsgenossenschaft der Bauwirtschaft Landsberger Strasse 309, 80687 Munich, GERMANY

Table 8: Cleaning of passenger trains, BGI 034

Title	Cleaning of passenger trains, BGI 5034
Type of project	Cleaning of passenger trains — risk assessment
Sector	Private cleaning contractors involved in cleaning passenger trains
Lead organisation	Berufsgenossenschaft der Straßen-, U-Bahnen und Eisenbahnen Fontenay 1 a, 20354 Hamburg, GERMANY
Others involved	Expert committee 'Rail transport' German states (Länder) Private contractors or companies Berufsgenossenschaft für Fahrzeughaltung (Institute for Statutory Accident Insurance and Prevention for Vehicle Operators) Berufsgenossenschaft der Bauwirtschaft (Institute for Statutory Accident Insurance and Prevention of the Building Industry) Hauptverband der Berufsgenossenschaften– HVBG (Federation of Institutions for Statutory Accident Insurance and Prevention)
Date of project	2007
Source of information	Website of Hauptverband der gewerblichen Berufsgenossenschaften (HVBG) in Kooperation mit dem Carl Heymanns Verlag http://www.arbeitssicherheit.de
Contact information	Berufsgenossenschaft der Straßen-, U-Bahnen und Eisenbahnen — BG BAHNEN Fontenay 1 a, 20354 Hamburg, GERMANY Tel. +49 4044118-0, Fax +49 4044118-240 E-mail: praev.hh@bg-bahnen.de http://www.bg-bahnen.de

3.6.4. BGI 835: A standard for railway vehicle washing plants

This guide was also produced by the 'rail transport' expert committee of the BG BAHNEN[48], specifically for those who work in specialised washing plants for railway carriages. BGI 835 was published in 2002. It covers cleaning work and risk assessment, along with means of access, boarding aids, lighting, electrical installations, work equipment, supply and proper disposal of cleaning products, waste disposal, and communication systems.

The document covers all the potentially significant health and safety related risks associated with the facilities, plant and technical equipment used to clean the interior of railway carriages.

The type of cleaning depends on the type of railway vehicle in question, and the quality requirements of the railway operators. Specialised equipment is needed to guarantee the quality and the cost-effectiveness of cleaning processes.

The different types of cleaning work include daily, weekly, basic, light to heavy cleaning and anything in between that the railway operators may require, including:

- dry-cleaning of floor, carpet, seats, equipment;
- cleaning of windows and all glass surfaces (inboard cleaning);
- removal of litter, debris and other materials;
- replenishing of materials and supplies (for instance towels, toilet paper, soap, etc.);
- wet cleaning of walls, ceiling, floor, sanitary facilities;
- cleaning of doorknobs and steps (inside and outside carriages).

The BG information brochure gives rail operators and their contractors, such as designers and planners, construction, maintenance and cleaning contractors, useful information about the planning and installation of washing plant for interior cleaning of passenger trains.

This document lists the safety and health requirements to be adhered to when planning or operating interior washing equipment in railway vehicles, as well as the BG rules.

48 Ibid.

Table 9: Washing plant for interior cleaning of railway vehicles installation and Technical equipment, BGI 835

Title	Washing plant for interior cleaning of railway vehicles — Installation and Technical Equipment, BGI 835
Type of project	Guide to assist railway operators or owners when planning or mounting washing facilities to clean railway carriages or vehicles
Sector	Target group is the cleaning industry but more particularly its contractors specialised in the cleaning of railway vehicles
Lead organisation	Berufsgenossenschaft der Straßen-, U-Bahnen und Eisenbahnen Fontenay 1 a, 20354 Hamburg, GERMANY
Others involved	Expert Committee 'Rail transport', German states private contractors or companies
Date of project	2002
Sources of information	Website of Hauptverband der gewerblichen Berufsgenossenschaften (HVBG) in Kooperation mit dem Carl Heymanns Verlag http://www.arbeitssicherheit.de Berufsgenossenschaft der Bauwirtschaft http://www.bgbau.de
Contact information	Berufsgenossenschaft der Straßen-, U-Bahnen und Eisenbahnen — BG BAHNEN Fontenay 1 a, 20354 Hamburg, GERMANY Tel. +49 4044118-0, Fax +49 4044118-240 E-mail: praev.hh@bg-bahnen.de http://www.bg-bahnen.de

3.7. A photo exhibition honouring cleaners (Germany)

- Exhibition of photos of cleaners at work and interviews covering issues like working time, clothes, safety and health, PPE, etc. (http://www.landkreis-wesermarsch.de/)
- Shown in city halls and other busy venues (http://www.zfg-oldenburg.de/)

3.7.1. Introduction

In 2001 a book entitled *Frauen in der Wesermarsch* (women in the Weser marsh) was published by the Wesermarsch rural district authority showing high-quality photographs of female cleaners in various work environments. Two years later the Zentrum für Frauengeschichte (centre for women's history) in Oldenburg turned these photos into an exhibition.

The project team decided to supplement the photos with interviews with the cleaners themselves, to give an extra dimension to the exhibition and give a voice to a category of workers who are normally voiceless.

3.7.2. Aims and objectives

The work of cleaners is only noticed when it is not carried out, e.g. when floors are covered with dirt. It is still viewed as a women's job, a continuation of unpaid housework.

This exhibition aimed to make the work of cleaners more visible, in the hope that the public would treat them with more consideration and have more respect for their job.

3.7.3. Scope of the project — what was done

The project team identified the challenges facing cleaners in their daily work. These included issues such as working time and conditions of employment, which vary considerably: in hospitals, cleaning is done early in the morning whereas in schools, offices, medical practices and supermarkets cleaners start work only after the other workers have left the premises. In factories, cleaners may work irregular shift systems parallel to the normal day shifts.

Cleaners want to leave their place of work in a clean and orderly state, but in some cases they do not have enough time to allow for this. This means the workers have to cope not only with having too little time for their work, but also with the frustration of knowing that they cannot do their job as well as they might. They also frequently have to remove dirt and litter which is deliberately dropped by people of all ages. The project team wanted to encourage companies and other institutions, schools and parents to establish rules on littering and apply them.

Numerous photos of cleaning staff doing their daily work are presented on 45 pages. The remaining 40 pages show a mixture of photos and interview texts with cleaners. The women explain their views on several topics. Some of the headlines read as follows.

- Working time — we also work on Sundays
- Working clothes — not the best stuff
- Working stress — the demands get heavier all the time
- Safety and health — I hate working with gloves anyway
- Contacts — mostly the people are alright, but there is no appreciation
- Fear — sometimes the building goes very quiet.

Cleaners' statements from the documentation

These are things which could be improved.

'This bending, always bending: bucket into the sink, fill it up and then lift it and put it down on the trolley and vice versa. If we had a drain we could empty it much easier at floor level. Then it is this up and down and this bent posture while cleaning desks. There are many things one could improve. Having a hosepipe on the tap to fill the bucket, for example. The same with the vacuum cleaner …These always fall down … one has to bend down to pick them up.'

'They don't care about us. They are so cheeky nowadays.

Sometimes they spit on the floor, because they don't see me and then they say: "Oh!" I say: "You do that at home also?" "No!" Or, when there is litter, I say: "Pick it up!" "No, why. I didn't throw it away!" Although I saw they did. They don't care about us. They are so cheeky nowadays. "And what are cleaners for, anyway?"'

The exhibition presents large photos (90 x 200 cm) of women cleaners at work, printed on tarpaulin, refuse bags, chamois and PVC tiles. There are explanations in texts and illustrations on topics like:

- from maid servant to cleaning women;
- professionalisation and standardisation of private and commercial cleaning;
- women office cleaners;
- the development of cleaning equipment;
- caricatures about cleaning.

The exhibition includes leaflets from the trade union Industriegewerkschaft Bauen-Agrar-Umwelt (IGBAU)[49] containing information on the minimum wage in four languages. There is usually an opening ceremony, with speeches and a cabaret programme. Often the cleaners of the building where the exhibition is held receive a special invitation to the opening.

3.7.4. Results and evaluation of the project

Despite having a limited budget, the exhibition was presented for the first time at the International Women's Day 2003 in Oldenburg. Until 2007 it was shown at about 20 places in Germany for about four to six weeks at each venue. Venues include museums and galleries, but the exhibition is mainly requested by gender officials and presented in the well-frequented foyers of city halls. The most visited location was the check-in area of Münster/Osnabrück airport.

3.7.5. Transferability of the project

The documentation — German language only — is available from Ms Bernhold (address below). The exhibition can be borrowed for a fee of EUR 500 per month from the ZFG (address below). In non-German speaking countries a translation would be necessary. It would also be necessary to explain some typical German working conditions.

49 http://www.igbau.de

3.7.6. Details of initiative

Table 10: Documentation

Title	*Putz munter* (Clean spirit) — Documentation *Bodenpersonal-putzen kann jede(r)!?'* (ground staff — everybody can clean!?) — Exhibition
Type of project	Photo documentation and exhibition
Sector	Cleaning
Lead organisation	Landkreis (rural district authority) Wesermarsch, Ulla Bernhold, Gleichstellungsbeauftragte (Equal gender opportunities officer)
Others involved	The documentation was sponsored by the German state of Lower Saxony
Date of project	Documentation prepared: 2001, exhibition from 2003 ongoing
Contact information	Ulla Bernhold, Gleichstellungsbeauftragte, Landkreis Wesermarsch — Frauenbüro Poggenburger Straße 15, 26919 Brake, GERMANY Tel. +49 4401/927-288, Fax +49 4401/3471 E-mail: gleichstellungsbeauftragte@lkbra.de ZFG- Zentrum für Frauen-Geschichte e.V. Cloppenburger Str. 71, 26135 Oldenburg, GERMANY Tel. +49 441/77 69 90 E-mail: info@zfg-oldenburg.de http://www.zfg-oldenburg.de

The GISBAU glove database (Germany) 3.8.

- Many hazardous materials used in the cleaning of buildings require use of gloves
- GISBAU database [50] enables easy selection of suitable protective gloves for the task

3.8.1. Introduction

Cleaners use a huge number of chemical cleaning agents, and the occurrence of skin diseases is on the increase. Because cleaning is usually carried out manually, there is often intensive skin contact with the products. Hence, protective gloves are usually worn by cleaners. This project investigated which gloves offer optimum protection in which circumstances.

GISBAU has been making recommendations on suitable glove materials for approximately 10 years. In cooperation with several glove manufacturers GISBAU developed a database that provides information on which gloves are most suitable for building cleaners and workers in other branches of the building industry.

50 GISBAU is the hazardous materials information service of BG BAU, the statutory accident insurance body for the German construction and services sector.

An increasing number of manufacturers are providing detailed specifications about suitable gloves in their safety datasheets, which include layer thickness as well as breakthrough or penetration times. However, specifying material only is not sufficient, as a recent research project pointed out[51]: the breakthrough times of gloves of the same type (e.g. latex or Nitrillatex) but from different manufacturers, can vary, even where the membrane strength is comparable. The breakthrough times can differ by 200–300 %. Therefore, a significant test can refer in each case only to a glove product and not inclusively to a type of polymer. For this reason the TRGS 220 'Security Datasheet' specifies that not only material, but penetration time of the glove material should be considered when selecting gloves[52].

3.8.2. Aims and objectives

The glove database is intended mainly for use by entrepreneurs and specialists in industrial safety in the cleaning sector. It provides cleaners with a practical instrument enabling them to determine easily the appropriate glove type for the cleaning agents they use. It is hoped that this will help reduce the incidence of skin disorders in the cleaning sector.

3.8.3. Scope of the project — what was done

First of all different glove manufacturers were asked whether they had the laboratory capacity to carry out glove tests, and whether they were prepared to do so. The manufacturers saw the potential benefits of the project and agreed to carry out the tests specified.

Several manufacturers of cleaning agents gave GISBAU samples of sanitary cleaning agents. Products typical of the respective GISBAU product groups were selected and labelled with a product code[53].

The products were then sent to the glove manufacturers with the request to issue glove product recommendations taking into account the use of the chemicals in practice. The manufacturers' recommendations were added to WINGIS, the hazardous material software produced by GISBAU.

Safety datasheets and technical product information were supplied along with the products. From this manufacturer information, the institutes were able to identify the dangerous substances in the cleaning agents. Above all they could also see how the products are processed on site.

3.8.4. Results and evaluation of the project

All tested gloves with a minimum layer thickness of 0.4 mm offered sufficient protection over more than eight hours with the sanitary cleaner concentrates tested. Thus, all tested gloves could be used for a full shift length when cleaning with diluted sanitary cleaners.

51 Forschungsbericht 'Chemikalienschutzhandschuhe', Hauptverband der gewerblichen Berufsgenossenschaften 1999 (http://www.hvbg.de/d/bia/pub/rep/rep01/pdf_datei/forsch/handsch.pdf).

52 TRGS 220, 'Sicherheitsdatenblatt', Technische Regeln für Gefahrstoffe, Ausgabe: Dezember 2006 (http://www.baua.de/nn_16700/de/Themen-von-A-Z/Gefahrstoffe/TRGS/pdf/TRGS-220.pdf).

53 Product code details are online (http://www.gisbau.de).

The pilot study[54] showed that companies were willing to cooperate. They compiled dependable data on chemicals, protective gloves and their fields of application even though the tests are time and cost-intensive.

Due to the large number of cleaning agents and other hazardous materials used in the building industry the approach used with the sanitary cleaning agents — carrying out laboratory tests with products from each individual product group — could not be used. Simplified strategies had to be found. The product group system created by GISBAU, in which comparable products are categorised together into GISCODEs or product codes, was employed instead. Under this system, thousands of products can be summarised into a manageable number of approximately 50 product groups.

Known glove manufacturers were asked to recommend appropriate gloves for different uses, with the help of the classification catalogue for cleaning and preservative agents. The classification catalogue lists the chemical compositions of the product groups. The recommendations had to indicate whether the chemical concerned should be used in diluted or concentrated form. In addition, the increased body temperature inside the glove had to be taken into account. Using these data, glove manufacturers had to come up with an optimum wearing time for the glove concerned.

Within six months GISBAU received data on wearing time recommendations for all cleaning and preservative agents (sanitary cleaning fluids, basic cleaning agents, disinfectants, etc.). A comparison with data from the pilot phase showed that the recommendations agreed with the test results.

Approximately 10 000 recommendations for wearing time for 188 glove products in the 55 product groups of the product code for cleaning and preservative agents were made available to GISBAU. This quantity of data could not be published in paper form so they were placed on an electronic database.

Today the databank is a permanent component of WINGIS, GISBAU's hazardous materials CD-ROM. WINGIS is made available annually to companies in the cleaning industry at no cost. The GISBAU glove database can be also found on the Internet[55] along with the online version of WINGIS[56].

The protective gloves database enables cleaning and building companies to select appropriate gloves for the task at hand quickly and easily. In the future this database will be expanded to include other chemicals including wood preservatives, seals, paints and varnishes.

54 Rheker, R., Musanke, U., Prüfung von Sanitärreinigern durch Handschuhhersteller zeigt Ansätze; rationell reinigen 11/2003, pp. 38–45.

55 http://www.gisbau.de

56 http://www.wingisonline.de

3.8.5. Details of initiative

Table 11: GISBAU glove database

Title	GISBAU glove database
Type of project	Database for 'off and online' use
Sector	Cleaning industry, construction industry
Lead organisation	Hazardous material information system of the Institute for Statutory Accident Insurance and Prevention of the Building Industry — GISBAU
Date of project	From 2006
Contact information	Reinhard Rheker, Dr Uwe Musanke Berufsgenossenschaft der Bauwirtschaft — GISBAU Hungener Str. 6, 60437 Frankfurt, GERMANY Tel. +49 694705-279, Fax +49 694705-288 E-mail: gisbau@bgbau.de http://www.gisbau.de

3.9. Network portal helps SMEs manage dangerous substances (Germany)

- Focus was hazardous substances used in the cleaning of buildings
- Aim to increase awareness of the many hazardous substances in use
- Support for SMEs by encouraging self-help
- Internet portal provides information about hazardous substances, virtual and real information network

3.9.1. Introduction

Hazardous substances are a multilayered problem in cleaning companies. Many different products are used in the modern cleaning industry. Cleaning contractors work in a variety of environments, ranging from office buildings to factories to hospitals. The cleaning products chosen depend upon the objects to be cleaned. The products that potentially contain hazardous substances range from strong bleaches to emulsions, wood and stone preservative agents, and industrial cleaners including formaldehyde-based disinfectants. Glass cleaning substances that are highly diluted are on the other hand relatively harmless.

The risk of harm is increased if the cleaners using the substances lack training or knowledge about the dangerous substances in use. The high number of skin diseases found among cleaners makes it clear that action needs to be taken. Handling hazardous substances without the necessary preventive measures can lead to skin damage or make the skin more susceptible to diseases. A special emphasis was therefore placed on building cleaners, who suffer a high incidence of skin diseases.

Experience has shown that SMEs, especially the smaller ones, tend to lack the skills and knowledge to deal with dangerous substances safely. Often the people in charge do not have enough information or they are not sufficiently qualified.

The 'Gefahrstoffe im Griff' (hazardous substances under control) portal aimed to close this knowledge gap. The project was carried out from January to September 2004 under the leadership of the State Institute for Occupational Safety and Health of North Rhine-Westphalia (LAfA)[57].

It was promoted by the EU-OSHA — European Agency for Safety and Health at Work.

In June 2005 four action aids on handling hazardous materials were published for small firms in the following trades: building cleaning; motor vehicle workshops; sanitary, heating and air conditioning technology; carpentry and joinery. From July 2005 to March 2006 firms in these sectors, principally small ones, were informed and advised about practical hazardous material management.

The action aids were developed and coordinated by the labour safety administration of North Rhine-Westphalia in cooperation with trade associations in the relevant industries, the Centre for environment and energy of Düsseldorf Chamber of trade and statutory accident insurance bodies.

3.9.2. Aims and objectives

The goal of this information and advice network was to bring together information providers and 'clients' in need of help with their risk management. The collected knowledge is easily accessible and presented in a simple, practical manner.

This helps companies get to grips with the legal requirements they must fulfil when working with hazardous substances; thus it helps promote health and safety among the workers, too.

3.9.3. Scope of the project — what was done

The core activity was the creation of a hazardous substances portal and communications network. The Gefahrstoffe im Griff network includes practical hazardous materials guidelines for various occupations and/or sectors. Users are able to pose questions to experts, and the portal has a series of checklists for practical use in the company concerned. The portal also includes downloadable presentations and address details of relevant companies/parties in the industry and related organisations.

3.9.4. Problems faced

Numerous requirements associated with the handling of cleaning agents meant that employers and workers in cleaning companies were misunderstanding the necessary preventive measures. Hence, it was decided to create a simple portal that could clear up the confusion without demanding too much of the users.

57 Landesanstalt für Arbeitsschutz NRW.

3.9.5. Success factors

The success of the project was primarily due to the fact that all the relevant participants are involved in the network. State health and safety officials, the statutory accident insurance bodies, trade associations and trade unions and medical associations made available their complementary knowledge to create a detailed and comprehensive resource.

The results from more than 1 000 company consultations underline how important it is to include companies and professional bodies in any activity aimed at SMEs.

The fact that all network partners were geographically close was a help because it made it possible to hold regular meetings.

Beside the 'virtual' information network developed by regional unions, safety consultants, professional organisations, chambers of commerce and other relevant bodies are now interlinked so they can act as contact points for SMEs requiring assistance.

The constantly high access figures for the portal and the positive feedback received confirm that the target groups are being reached. The portal was getting about 20 000 visitors per month in spring 2007.

'Tiptop in NRW, Dangerous materials — but safe!' is a brochure developed to accompany the project. It is available online[58] and attempts to explain in simple language the dangers from materials used in building cleaning.

3.9.6. Transferability of the project

This project is transferable to other regions and countries in the European Union as the idea of bring together all participants of a region into a network is transmittable. German peculiarities, for example the operating instructions, could be adapted, if necessary, in revised form or be substituted for regionally appropriate guidelines.

58 NRW stands for North-Rhine Westphalia (http://www.gefahrstoffe-im-griff.de).

3.9.7. Details of initiative

Table 12: Landesanstalt für Arbeitsschutz Nordrhein-Westfales (LAfA)

Lead organisation	Landesanstalt für Arbeitsschutz Nordrhein-Westfalen (LAfA) (State Institute for Occupational Safety and Health of North Rhine-Westphalia)
Others involved	ASER — Institute for Occupational Medicine, Safety and Ergonomics, Wuppertal UZH — Düsseldorf Chamber of Small Industries and Skilled Trades, Düsseldorf TBS — Technical Advisory Office of the German Trade Union Confederation, Oberhausen BAuA — Federal Institute for Occupational Safety and Health, Dortmund StAfA — Workplace Health and Safety Offices in Aachen and Essen BGW — Institute for Statutory Accident Insurance and Prevention for the Healthcare Sector Promoted by the European Agency for Safety and Health at Work
Further information	Project 'Controlling dangerous substances: building a support network for SMEs' published in: *Promoting health and safety in European Small and Medium-sized Enterprises (SMEs)*, Luxembourg: Office for Official Publications of the European Communities, 2005, ISBN 92-9191-141-0, © EU-OSHA — European Agency for Safety and Health at Work, 2005
Contact details	Dr Werner Ködel, Dr Kai Seiler, Landesanstalt für Arbeitsschutz Nordrhein-Westfalen Ulenbergstraße 127–131, 40225 Düsseldorf, GERMANY Tel. +49 2113101-2251, Fax +49 213101-2228 E-mail: koedel@lafa.nrw.de http://www.gefahrstoffe-im-griff.de http://www.arbeitsschutz.nrw.de http://www.arbeitsschutz.nrw.de/lafa

3.10. Moving with Awareness — an ergonomic approach to training cleaners (Germany)

- Training concept for cleaning personnel: 'Moving with Awareness'
- Concept established and developed through several projects aimed at improving health and safety for cleaners
- Cleaners learn how to avoid strenuous movements and postures

3.10.1. Introduction

This award-winning training concept (IAS 2001) was developed in collaboration with cleaners by Professor Elke Huth and others, and has been tested successfully several times in different cleaning companies.

Studies in the late 1990s at the University of Applied Science Hamburg identified specific sources of stress and overexertion in cleaning staff. These factors appear to correlate with negative technical and organisational conditions at the workplace.

Improving observation skills

Participants have to recognise different working postures and provide commentary on their selection.

4. Practise with working equipment — participants get into small groups to practise using their work equipment while employing optimal techniques. In this phase the trials and assessments by participants and the instructor are emphasised. The cleaners are also encouraged to take photos of each other while practising. Where appropriate new equipment might have to be purchased, e.g. mops with telescopic handles.
5. Reflect through reinforcing activity.
6. Practise at the work site — it might be found necessary to purchase new equipment e.g. mops with telescopic handles.

3.10.4. Results and evaluation of the project

Through a follow-up study[61] 50 trainers in the 'Moving with Awareness' concept have confirmed that the teaching and implementation of the concept has been effective. In addition 100 trainees were asked to participate in the programme evaluation. In summary, they found the training concept valuable in increasing awareness and easing burdens at work.

Table 13: Changes

Variable	Changes
Social recognition	Improved communication among one another and with supervisory staff
Work-related reflection	Seeing with awareness, adaptive work behaviour according to setting evident
Development of personnel	Acceptance of new responsibilities and tasks
Organisational changes	Participation in changing work sequences
Technical changes	Participation in recommending new equipment

61 Huth, Elke, Gesund und Sicher — Entwicklung und Integration eines Lernkonzeptes: Bewusst bewegen' beim Reinigen, Abschlussbericht, 1999.

3.10.5. Success factors

The success of such a project depends greatly on the level of integration into the overall organisational structure and the level of commitment of the supervisors, various levels of management and the specialists in occupational and health and safety, including company physicians and human resource personnel.

3.10.6. Transferability of the project

The concept can be applied in all countries and regions. It is available in English and German. The material for participants is also available in Turkish.

3.10.7. Details of initiative

Table 14: Moving with Awareness — An ergonomic approach to training cleaning personnel

Title	Moving with Awareness — An ergonomic approach to training cleaning personnel
Social recognition	Training concept
Sector	Cleaning
Lead organisation	University of Applied Sciences Hamburg Professor Elke Huth Tel. +49 40826518 E-mail: elkehuth@gmx.net
Others involved	Health insurer, accident insurer, labour inspectorate, equipment manufacturers
Date of project	1997, 2000 evaluated, ongoing active project
Contact information	Professor Elke Huth, University of Applied Sciences Hamburg Tel. +49 40826518, E-mail: elkehuth@gmx.net http://www.bewegungs-abc.de

3.11. Vocational training for cleaners (KMK) (Germany)

- Building cleaning is an approved profession in Germany
- Vocational training takes place in a dual system in companies and vocational schools
- Personal and social skills are taught in addition to occupational skills
- Vocational schools have to include occupational safety topics in their curricula

3.11.1. Introduction

In Germany, the cleaning of buildings is a recognised profession with approved education. The education takes place in a dual system both in the workplace and at the vocational school. The vocational schools aim to:

- teach occupational skills along with general personal and social skills;
- develop the professional flexibility to cope with the changing requirements in professional life and society, particularly the creation of a single European market;
- integrate teaching about health and safety at work into various aspects of the curriculum.

3.11.2. Scope of the project — what was done

The ministers of education and the arts and culture senators of the states (KMK) in the Federal Republic of Germany created a framework curriculum regulating the goals and contents of vocational education for all federal states based largely on the secondary school certificate and describing minimum requirements. The curriculum encourages independent and responsible thinking and behaviour in all areas of education. However, the framework does not specify detailed content for each lesson.

Table 15: Overview of the curriculum for the training of a building cleaner

Learning field	Lessons (time values in hours)			
	Year 1	Year 2	Year 3	Total
Treating of non-textile floors	120			120
Treating of textile surfaces	80			80
Cleaning of glass surfaces	80			80
Treating of sanitary areas		100		100
Treating of public health areas		60		60
Cleaning of electric-technical equipment		60		60
Cleaning and care of exterior installations and traffic guiding devices		60		60
Treating of façades			120	120
Cleaning of vehicles			40	40
Cleaning of industrial premises			40	40
Combating germs and vermin			80	80
Total	280	280	280	840

3.11.3. Results, evaluation, and transferability of the project

Between 1999 and 2005, 5 801 apprentices completed training as building cleaners. Thirteen percent of them were women. These figures make it clear that most of the approximately 900 000 cleaning workers in German have no comprehensive professional training. The transferability of this initiative will depend on whether vocational education is organised on similar lines to the German system in other states.

3.11.4. Details of the project

Table 16: Vocational training for cleaners (KMK)

Title	Vocational training for cleaners (KMK)
Type of project	Framework curriculum for the profession with approved education building cleaner
Lead organisation	Ständige Konferenz der Kultusminister und -senatoren der Länder (KMK) (Permanent Conference of the Ministers of Education and the Arts and Cult Senators of the States)
Date of project	1999 onwards
Contact information	Responsible body for vocational education (State of Hessen): Landesfachschule Hessen des Gebäudereiniger-Handwerks (Technical School of Hessen for the Building Cleaner Handicraft) Heinz-Herbert-Karry-Strasse 4, 60389 Frankfurt, GERMANY Tel. +49 69477700, Fax +49 69476100
Further information	http://www.kmk.org Frame CURRICULUM for the profession with approved education building cleaner (Resolution of the Conference of the Ministers of Education and the Arts and Cult senators of the States from 25 March 1999): http://www.kmk.org/beruf/rlpl/rlpgr.pd Curriculum for the Federal State of North Rhine-Westphalia (exemplarily): http://www.bildungsportal.nrw.de/BP/Schulrecht/RuL/RuLProbe/Bk/Berufe/Gebaeudereiniger.pdf

3.12. Creating a quality management system for a cleaning contractor (Germany)

- Cleaning contractor wanted to link the aspects of quality, health and environmental protection in its management
- Measures from existing quality management standards were used as a basis, adapted to the company's particular needs
- Lost hours due to back complaints were reduced to nearly nil by the introduction of telescopic handles
- Training of employees was structured and intensified

3.12.1. Introduction

Cleaning contractor KARO-Gebäudereinigungs GmbH carried out this project with support from the German Bundesanstalt für Arbeitsschutz und Arbeitsmedizin — BAuA (Federal Institute for Occupational Safety and Health), with the help of the Hamburg Chamber of Trade.

Existing standards (DIN EN ISO 9000 ff for quality management, DIN EN ISO 14001 for environmental management and requirements based on the framework directive for

a safety management system) have comparable elements to the system the company intended to introduce.

When introducing an integrated management system it is important to consider four elements in particular:

- management responsibility
- process orientation
- prevention/improvement
- participation.

For any management system to be accepted and effective in the long term, it must be specific to the individual company. The aim was to adapt the existing standards to make them appropriate for this enterprise.

3.12.2. Aims and objectives

The aim was to implement an integrated management system in a service company that included industrial safety, health protection and environment protection. The new system would include existing elements of a quality management system according to DIN EN ISO 9001. The project also sought to strengthen the prevention measures to help reduce the number of work-related accidents and ailments.

3.12.3. Scope of the project — what was done

The KARO Gebäudereinigungs GmbH, founded in 1986, had about 600 employees at the start of this project. It had begun the process of DIN EN ISO 9001 certification, but the company's management felt that this did not go far enough to integrate safety and health protection, prevention and environmental protection. It wanted to develop an integrated management system that seamlessly linked all these important factors.

Actions

Developing and adapting a management system is a company-wide task, and it is important to ensure that the workers are integrated into the process. The development can be divided roughly into three phases.

1. The employees are informed about the objectives of the process.
2. Interviews take place in the workplace or in group meetings. Because not all employees are involved all the time, it is important to inform them regularly about the progress being made. At this point small and medium enterprises usually depend on external help in meeting basic conditions (laws, standards, regulations, etc.).
3. The third phase includes discussions of the draft plans, which are revised and reviewed to check their suitability in the everyday work situation.

Documenting the management system

Compliance with agreed regulations must be documented to define a clear company organisation. Documentation is seen by many SMEs as an unnecessary expense, but it has many advantages:

- it helps explain the management system and the workflow;

- it improves communication within the company;
- it cuts down on the likelihood of work being unnecessarily repeated;
- it can help motivate employees;
- it offers proof for customers and external inspectors that the company is achieving its intended standards.

The agreed regulations are described in the management manual.

3.12.4. Results and evaluation of the project

The integrated management system implemented by KARO has now been in operation for more than 10 years and is under constant development. In 1998 the system was certified according to DIN EN ISO 9001.

A central goal of KARO's management system was to increase safety at work. Over the course of time many of the early measures have been changed and adapted to make them more effective in achieving this aim. However, others have proved so satisfactory that they remain unchanged.

For example, the skin protection scheme, developed by a large manufacturer of hygiene products in cooperation with KARO, is still used by the cleaning workers in its original form. Over the years the effects of this measure have been recorded. The rate of skin diseases due to allergic reactions has fallen from 3 % to 0 %. This is an outstanding achievement in the building cleaning industry, and the company has reaped benefits in terms of cost savings and worker satisfaction.

Another preventive measure that has benefited the company was the introduction of telescopic mop handles for short cleaners. A risk assessment showed that workers of below average height suffered from back ailments because their cleaning tools were too big. Using overlong mops meant they had to apply considerable downward pressure and adopt non-ergonomic working postures. This put too much pressure on their back muscles and could lead to long-term back complaints. All fixed handles were substituted with telescope ones to enable each cleaner to adjust the handle individually according to their height. The number of working hours lost because of back complaints has been reduced to nearly nil.

In the in-house training centre newly employed cleaners are trained to work with cleaning equipment and materials before they start working at the customer sites. There is no time limit on the training and it can be carried out at a pace that suits the workers concerned.

In 2004 Hamburg Chamber of Commerce named KARO as the city's 'family-friendliest company'.

The system brought about a number of positive changes:

- it made the organisation and meaning of safety and health protection at work clearer and more transparent;
- through a proper risk assessment it made company-specific adjustments that helped prevent accidents and diseases;
- it raises the training level and quality of work among employees;
- it relies on written, detailed specifications that can be transferred easily;
- the documentation increases in volume, but makes it easier to prove that the necessary standards are being met.

3.12.5. Details of initiative

Table 17: Promoting OSH by adapting a quality management system for a cleaning contractor

Title	Promoting safety and health at work by adapting a quality management system for a cleaning contractor
Type of project	Integration of safety and health protection at work into a quality management system Brochure: *Bundesanstalt für Arbeitsschutz und Arbeitsmedizin* (Integrated management system in the building cleaning trade), 4th updated edition, Dortmund 2005, ISBN 3-88261-496-X
Sector	Building cleaning company
Lead organisation	Gewerbeförderung Handwerkskammer Hamburg GmbH Thomas Schulz
Others involved	Bundesanstalt für Arbeitsschutz und Arbeitsmedizin (BAuA)
Date of project	1997, last evaluation 2004
Contact information	Thomas Schulz Gewerbeförderung Handwerkskammer Hamburg GmbH Holstenwall 12, 20355 Hamburg, GERMANY Tel. +49 4035905-270, Fax +49 4035905-295 E-mail: thschulz@hwk-hamburg.de

3.13. A risk assessment guide for building cleaners — Hamburg (Germany)

- Risk assessment guide for building cleaners
- Evaluation according to Biological Substances Ordinance and Hazardous Substances Ordinance

3.13.1. Introduction

The Amt für Arbeitsschutz, Hamburg (Industrial safety authority of the city of Hamburg), with the Institute for Statutory Accident Insurance and Prevention of the building industry[62] and the Hamburg State Guild of building cleaners[63] carried out a project in 2006 and 2007 to prepare risk assessment guides for building cleaners.

3.13.2. Aims and objectives

Goals of the project were:

- to determine whether risk assessments were being carried out and how effective they were;

62 Berufsgenossenschaft der Bauwirtschaft — (BG BAU).

63 Landesinnung der Gebäudereiniger Hamburg.

- to find out how the Hazardous substances ordinance (GefStoffV) and the Biological substances ordinance (BioStoffV) are applied in practice in businesses.

To carry out a systematic and complete risk assessment businesses must take into account company-specific conditions and risks as well as general risks.

3.13.3. Scope of the project — what was done

Hamburg's industrial safety authority wanted to ensure that safety systems in place matched the needs of the companies concerned.

Employees of the authority visited 25 companies employing 9 000 part and full-time workers, and asked questions concerning safety and health protection at work. Topics included:

- the organisation of safety management;
- ergonomics of the tools used by cleaners, because of a disproportionately high incidence of MSDs among cleaners;
- skin disorders caused by contact with hazardous substances during cleaning;
- infection threats posed by certain activities;
- psychological stress and resultant lost working time.

3.13.4. Results and evaluation of the project

The study found that essential requirements of safety at work were being fulfilled in about 30% of companies. Around half the companies were carrying out adequate risk assessments and compiling the associated documentation.

Many companies have ended the use of hazardous substances for maintenance and cleaning work. Adequate instructions for the handling of hazardous substances in the languages of the employees were present in 60 % of the companies surveyed.

In 60 % of companies there was adequate coordination between clients and building cleaners concerning preventive measures at work. These companies saw themselves as obliged not only to fulfil quality criteria, but to protect the interest of their own staff. For example, staff are familiarised with emergency escape plans, in the event of a fire.

There is some uncertainty over areas of responsibility in the industry. For example, many cleaning contractors require their staff to wear a corporate uniform and have it cleaned at their own expense. However, when cleaning is done in toilets and sanitary facilities these clothes can also be regarded as protective clothing. In this case, the employer is responsible for cleaning the clothes.

Regular external supervision is carried out by an independent test institute. After a successful test report, the quality standards committee recommends the awarding of the quality mark. Inspection is repeated annually.

3.14.4. Results and evaluation of the project

The RAL building cleaning quality mark helps member firms stand out from the many competing cleaning contractors in the market. The mark was introduced in 1991. At the end of 2006, 43 building cleaning contractors held the mark.

3.14.5. Challenges

The Quality Association of Building Cleaners had to establish itself as a statutory organisation with at least seven members according to German law. The members come from organisations with different cultures, which can complicate the drawing up of quality and testing guidelines. There are concerns over the value of the RAL quality mark as to date, there are only 43 members of the quality association.

3.14.6. Success factors

For clients who have to tender work to cleaning contractors, getting one with RAL certification means they don't have to do their own inspection work. In particularly sensitive or high-security areas, having a quality approved cleaning contractor provides an extra layer of security.

3.14.7. Transferability of the project

RAL-GZ 902 was developed and introduced under the umbrella of the RAL. In the broadest sense it is a management audit with approved certification. In other European countries, comparable organisations with similar quality marks exist. There is no reason, therefore, why they could not come up with a similar standard adapted to local conditions.

3.14.8. Details of initiative

Table 19: Rules and regulations of the quality assured building cleaning — RAL

Title	Rules and regulations of the quality assured building cleaning — RAL-GZ 902 'Building cleaning'
Type of project	Quality mark
Sector	Building cleaning
Lead organisation	Gütegemeinschaft Gebäudereinigung e.V. (Quality Association of Building Cleaning)
Others involved	RAL Deutches Institut für gütesicherung und kennzeichnung e.V. (German Institute for Quality Assurance and Certifications)
Date of project	1991
Contact information	Gütegemeinschaft Gebäudereinigung e.V. (Quality Association of Building Cleaning) Stuttgarter Straße 3, 73525 Schwäbisch Gmünd, GERMANY Tel. +49 71711040840, Fax +49 71711040850, E-mail: Info@gggr.de

BGR 208: Protecting cleaners from infection risks in healthcare facilities (Germany) 3.15.

- High infection risks in healthcare facilities (e.g. contracting infections such as Hepatitis B from carelessly disposed of needles or syringes)
- Cleaners are particularly vulnerable to these risks
- This standard provides guidance on risk assessment, preventative and protection measures

3.15.1. Introduction

In Germany, private cleaning firms or contractors are insured by the Berufsgenossenschaft der Bauwirtschaft — BG BAU (Institute for Statutory Accident Insurance and Prevention of the building industry). The industrial cleaning sector includes a cleaning service specialising in healthcare facilities and premises where the infection risks are particularly high, for example from handling discarded hypodermic needles or syringes contaminated with blood or body fluids.

The specific requirements for controlling infection risks faced by cleaning staff arise from Directive 2000/54/EC. It deals with the risk of infection from handling biological, pathogenic or contaminated waste (including used needles/syringes) causing, for example, Hepatitis B. It also describes the measures to be taken and the procedures to be followed in case of accidental contamination.

The risks faced by cleaning staff in critical healthcare areas have often been overlooked and neglected, and the BGR[67] standard focuses on cleaning work in critical care areas such as operating theatres, isolation wards or dialysis rooms, where the infection risks are particularly high (needlestick injuries, puncture wounds).

3.15.2. Aims and objectives

The intention of this rule, first published in 2002 and updated in 2006, was to encourage cleaning contractors and cleaning staff particularly exposed to infection risks to take preventive measures (in getting the appropriate vaccine for hepatitis immunisation, for example) by;

- identifying the critical care areas;
- clearly defining the legal duties of cleaning firms and the contracting hospital or healthcare institute;
- giving the cleaning contractors the legal means to implement their hygiene or preventative plan.

67 'BG' is the acronym for 'Berufsgenossenschaft' — institute for statutory accident insurance and prevention — and 'R' stands for rule.

3.15.3. Details of initiative

Table 20: Exposure of cleaning staff to infection risks in healthcare facilities, BGR 208

Title	Exposure of cleaning staff to infection risks in healthcare facilities, BGR 208
Type of project	Exposure of cleaning staff to infection risks in healthcare facilities — Risk assessment
Sector	Private cleaning contractors involved in the cleaning of healthcare facilities and premises
Lead organisation	Berufsgenossenschaft der Bauwirtschaft Landsberger Strasse 309, 80687 Munich, GERMANY
Others involved	Expert Committee 'Civil Engineering' German states Berufsgenossenschaft für Gesundheitsdienst und Wohlfahrtspflege — BGW (Institutions for statutory accident insurance and prevention for the Healthcare Sector) Hauptverband der Berufsgenossenschaften — HVBG (Federation of institutions for statutory accident insurance and prevention) Companies
Date of project	First published in 2002; updated 2006
Further information	Website of Hauptverband der gewerblichen Berufsgenossenschaften (HVBG) in Kooperation mit dem Carl Heymanns Verlag: http://www.arbeitssicherheit.de *Berufsgenossenschaft der Bauwirtschaft* website: http://www.bgbau.de
Contact person	Dr Ursula Schies, Berufsgenossenschaft der Bauwirtschaft Landsberger Strasse 309, 80687 Munich, GERMANY Tel. +49 898897-872, Fax +49 898897-829

3.16. BGR 209: Rule on exposure to cleaning and care products (Germany)

- Rule to help assess risks to building cleaners from care products and substances
- Focus on wet work
- Enables assessment of risks in different cleaning environments

3.16.1. Introduction

Rule BGR 209 of the German statutory accident insurances covers all the specific regulatory requirements for handling cleaning agents and equipment used to clean premises or buildings and structures.

Cleaning products can pose health risks as they may contain corrosive or caustic chemicals causing skin problems, breathing difficulties and other conditions. The concentrated forms of some cleaning or care products are classified as hazardous so that the safety measures laid down in the Gefahrstoffverordnung — (German Hazardous Substances Ordinance — GefStoffV) must be complied with.

The regulations on work in specific environments (e.g. schools, sanitary facilities) are analysed case by case, as they require different types of preventive measures. Wet work is also covered in detail, as it can worsen the effects of cleaning agents containing hazardous substances.

3.16.2. Aims and scope

The aim of the rule is to help in the identification and assessment of the risks associated with the use of cleaning and care products containing health-impairing or hazardous substances. The requirements of the Hazardous Substances Ordinance that are of particular importance to cleaning contractors were collated into a set of rules to help employers and cleaning staff to take appropriate safety measures.

3.16.3. Details of initiative

Table 21: Exposure to cleaning and care products, BGR 209

Title	Exposure to cleaning and care products, BGR 209
Type of project	Rules on exposure to cleaning and care products
Sector	Private contractors in cleaning industry
Lead organisation	'Building' expert committee of BG BAU (Institute for Statutory Accident Insurance and Prevention of the building industry)
Others involved	German states
Date of project	Published October 2001
Contact information	Dr Claudia Waldinger, Expert Committee 'Building', Berufsgenossenschaft der Bauwirtschaft http://www.bgbau.de

DIN 77400: A QUALITY STANDARD FOR CLEANING SCHOOL BUILDINGS (GERMANY) 3.17.

- Standards regulate the relationship between client and contractor
- The contractor must fulfil criteria on company organisation and qualifications of cleaning workers
- The contractor should consider charging higher prices when the building to be cleaned is not ergonomically designed, because this makes the job harder for cleaners
- Knowledge of the standard might lead to optimised planning of buildings with cleaning in mind

3.17.1. Introduction

In 1999 Germany's Umweltbundesamt (Federal Environment Agency) stated that the standards of hygiene at some German schools needed improving [68]. As a result the Bundesinnungsverband des Gebäudereiniger-Handwerks (Federal Association of Trade Guilds of Building Cleaners) encouraged the development of German Standard DIN 77400 'Cleaning services — School buildings — Requirements for cleaning', which regulates the procurement of cleaning services, assessment of the scope of the job and requirements for the actual cleaning work and the desired results.

The standard indirectly affects the health and safety of cleaning staff because it advises that certain onerous working methods and hazardous materials should be avoided.

The building operator and the cleaning service, whether external or in-house, have to agree objective standards on how the cleaning will be done, for example relating to the frequency of cleaning and the machines and cleaning agents to be used. Apart from ensuring that the work is done to a predetermined standard, these stipulations help procurers of cleaning services to evaluate competitive tenders for the cleaning work.

3.17.2. Aims and scope of the project

It is the goal of this standard to define principles for appropriate, environmentally conscious and hygienic school cleaning. The initiative began in 1999 and the standard was adopted in September 2003.

A working committee of the Standardisation Committee 'Gebrauchstauglichkeit und Dienstleistungen' (NAGD) (Serviceability and Services) compiled standard DIN 77400. Groups involved included representatives of municipalities, parents, building cleaning companies, suppliers and research institutes. An address list of these institutions is given in Appendix C of the standard.

3.17.3. Results and evaluation of the project

In the standard, criteria are fixed for the evaluation of the object to be cleaned; in this case, school buildings. The criteria define the minimum cleaning requirements and expenditure as well as special requirements arising from use of the building by pupils.

Relevance of this standard for building cleaners

The standard sets specific targets, for example:

- the dust level must be kept within reasonable limits by, for example, damp wiping (because of the allergy risk and the danger of sliding on dusty floors);
- the cleaning contractors must have comprehensive knowledge, experience and skills as well as the necessary equipment, machinery and cleaning agents;
- the cleaning work must be carried out to the highest levels possible when it comes to environmental awareness and safety;
- machines must conform to valid safety regulations, and inspected to ensure this is the case.

68 Pressemeldung des Umweltbundesamtes aus dem Internet (www.umweltbundesamt.de/uba-info-presse/pressemitteilungen/p-2199-d.htm).

In Appendix B of the standard, the Objektaufnahmebogen (checklist for cleaning service providers), many factors are itemised that reduce expenditure on cleaning (as well as the physical load on the cleaning workers):

- chairs can be suspended from tables; it is not necessary to lift them on to the tabletop and down afterwards;
- there are storerooms on every floor with enough room for cleaning machines, water and power connections and adequate ventilation;
- automatic cleaning machines can be used, as well as bevels or elevators intended for wheelchair users;
- plug sockets are short distances apart;
- water taps are placed at least 50 cm high, enabling easy filling of wheel-mounted buckets;
- walls, flooring and furniture are as smooth and untextured as possible to ensure that they do not get too dirty; hence gentler cleaning agents can be used.

According to the Baustellenrichtlinie (building site guidelines[69]), at the planning and execution phase plans have to be drawn up for the future maintenance of the building. Planners of school buildings are now able to consult DIN 77400 as a basis. The standard makes it clear that the non-ergonomic layout of objects for cleaning purposes can lead to increased maintenance costs later on. It therefore pays to optimise building planning with a view to economical cleaning when the building is completed. German cleaning industry federations strongly emphasise this point in their publications[70].

3.17.4. Success factors

The industry federations and institutions directly concerned with the cleaning industry were involved in the creation of this standard. Consensus was achieved on all sides, which led to greater acceptance of the standard.

The federal association representing commercial building cleaners believes that DIN 77400 could serve as a basis for future procurement of cleaning services in schools. The association has published a special edition of the standard. It also includes a free checklist for cleaning service providers.

3.17.5. Transferability of the project

Standards institutions exist in all European countries. As a general principle, the drawing up of standards should involve a representative cross-section of all interest groups concerned.

A broad spectrum of organisations, institutions and interest groups was involved in the development of DIN 77400. The precise composition of the respective committees concerned are likely to differ in other countries according to local circumstances; the important thing however is that they are truly representative.

69 German implementation of the Council Directive 92/57/EEC of 24 June 1992 on the implementation of minimum safety and health requirements at temporary or mobile construction sites (eighth individual directive within the meaning of Article 16(1) of Directive 89/391/EEC) (http://eurlex.europa.eu/smartapi/cgi/sga_doc?smartapi!celexapi!prod!CELEXnumdoc&lg=EN&numdoc=31992L0057&model=quichett).

70 See Henrich, M. et al., Bauplanung und Reinigungstechnik (Building design and cleaning technology), Landesinnung Hessen Gebäudereiniger-Handwerk.

3.17.6. Details of initiative

Table 22: Deutsche Norm DIN 77400

Title	Deutsche Norm DIN 77400 'Reinigungsdienstleistungen — Schulgebäude — Anforderungen an die Reinigung'
Type of project	Development and publication of a standard
Sector	Building cleaning, schools, public client
Lead organisation	DIN Deutsches Institut für Normung e.V., Normenausschuss Gebrauchstauglichkeit und Dienstleistungen (NAGD) Arbeitssausschuss NAGD-AA 4.2 'Anforderungen an die Reinigung von Schulgebäuden' (German Institute for Standardisation e.V. (DIN), Standardisation Committee Serviceability and Services (NAGD) working committee NAGD-AA 4.2 Requirements for the cleaning of school buildings)
Others involved	Bundesinnungsverband des Gebäudereiniger-Handwerks (Federal association of trade guilds of building cleaners), Bonn; representatives of cleaning sector Kommunale Gemeinschaftsstelle (Municipal partnership agency), Cologne; representatives of operators of school buildings; Parental representatives
Date of project	1999–2003
Further information	Copyright of the standard: Beuth Verlag GmbH, Berlin Special edition available through: Bundesinnungsverband des Gebäudereiniger-Handwerks (Federal association of building cleaner trade guilds), Dottendorfer Straße 86, 53129 Bonn, GERMANY Tel. +49 228917750, Fax +49 2289177511 E-mail: biv@gebaeudereiniger.de www.gebaeudereiniger.de
Contact information	Normenausschuss Gebrauchstauglichkeit und Dienstleistungen (NAGD) im DIN Deutsches Institut für Normung e.V., Burggrafenstr. 6, 10787 Berlin, GERMANY Tel. +49 302601-0, E-mail: info@din.de http://www.din.de

3.18. Collective agreement for building cleaners Madrid (Spain)

- Collective agreements are developed by the social partners
- Accepted by state authorities and binding for the whole sector
- Collective agreements can contain regulations to improve safety and health at the workplace

3.18.1. Introduction

Collective agreements for the cleaning industry exist in much of Spain. These agreements are negotiated between the social partners — trade unions and professional associations. The authorities check that the agreements adhere to labour laws, after which they are ratified. The collective agreements then form binding

regulations for the sector, generally on a local or regional basis. These collective agreements regulate not only the payment for cleaning workers, but many other issues relating to working conditions. This is an example of one cleaning collective agreement, 'Cleaning of buildings and premises', Madrid, released 2005.

3.18.2. Aims and objectives

This collective agreement regulated working conditions for all companies, and their employees, involved in cleaning buildings and premises, even if this is not their main activity. It was valid for three years, ending 31 December 2007.

3.18.3. Scope of the project — what was done

The two partners negotiated the terms of the planned collective agreement. They then submitted their agreement to the authorities for formal ratification as a collective agreement binding for all companies and employees of that region and sector.

3.18.4. Results and evaluation of the project

The collective agreement requires that vacancies must, if possible, be filled with unemployed workers from the sector itself. Workers are obliged to report any defect or malfunction of their equipment to their superiors to maintain the quality of the service, while they have rights that include being professionally educated at work and not suffering discrimination e.g. on the grounds of gender, civil status, religion, membership of a union, etc.

The collective agreement contains a classification of professional categories of staff. Six professional categories are determined. The relevant groups for cleaning companies are as follows.

Middle managers

- Supervisor or person in charge of a sector — a sector consists of two or more persons in charge of a group of workers or a building. Supervisors have to organise the staff so that they perform efficiently and are not overloaded.
- Attendant of a group or building — an attendant is in charge of 10 or more cleaners and has to allocate the work in such a way that the cleaners do not become fatigued.

Members of the group of working staff

- The specialist, a worker over 18, who operates any equipment and industrial machines with full theoretical and practical knowledge.
- The specialised worker or window cleaner, older than 18 years. They have to carry out cleaning tasks that require certain practical experience and specialisation and may involve danger or risks.
- The cleaners have to clean by hand with traditional or mechanised equipment that is easy to use. They should not do work that requires too much attention or physical effort.

The ordinary maximum working time is 39 hours of effective work per week. For workers who work at night this working time is reduced by two hours. The workday cannot be split into more than two shifts. In each period worked, the transfer from one workplace to another has to be counted as working time, unless the workplaces

are within the same business district. Further regulations exist in the collective agreement concerning holidays, maternity leave and job protection.

One chapter of the collective agreement is dedicated to safety and health at work. As a general principle the two parties commit to promoting as many measures as necessary to ensure adequate protection of the health of the workers. The chapter covers the evaluation of risks, preventive planning, the provision of information and training, health protection, and the protection of particularly vulnerable workers from specific risks. Other parts of the chapter deal with personal protective equipment, working clothes and the handling of loads.

3.18.5. Problems faced

Both social partners, employers and unions, have to form a commission in which each party has equal numbers of representatives. Any dispute over the collective agreement must be solved by them without recourse to legal means and under the supervision of the Instituto Laboral de la Comunidad de Madrid.

3.18.6. Success factors

The collective agreement was initiated by the social partners of the cleaning sector: the trade unions and professional associations. It focuses heavily on safety and health and social working conditions. Because collective agreements are put in force by the authorities, they become binding even for companies that do not regard safety and health as priorities.

3.18.7. Transferability of the project

The use of collective agreements to improve the working conditions of cleaners might be transferable to other European nations, with locally appropriate modifications, as in Germany.

A collective agreement requires a (strong) union and employers' association for the sector. A collective agreement made by them is binding for the contractors and their members on both sides — organised workers and companies affiliated to the employer association. In most countries the rate of unionisation in the cleaning sector is not that high. In Germany it is estimated to be only around 7 %[71]. Thus, a collective agreement can only have an impact on the working conditions of the whole sector if national legislation allows for a collective agreement to be declared binding for all employers and employees, regardless of whether they are organised into unions.

The collective agreement for Madrid is available online[72]. Access to all Spanish regional collective agreements of the cleaning industry is also available through El Portal Oficial de la Limpieza Profesional[73].

71 Schürmann, Lena; Schroth, Heidi, 'Nicht nur ein bisschen dreckig', Freitag 15, Die Ost-West-Zeitung, 2.4.2004, Berlin Zeitungsverlag 'Freitag' GmbH, ISSN 0945-2095 (http://www.freitag.de/2004/15/04151701.php).

72 El Portal Oficial de la Limpieza Profesional (http://www.1a3soluciones.com/convenios/CONVENIOMADRID.htm).

73 CONVENIOS COLECTIVOS PROVINCIALES de limpieza de Edificios y Locales (http://www.1a3soluciones.com/convenios/convenios.asp).

3.18.8. Details of initiative

Table 23: Collective agreements for the sector 'Cleaning of buildings and premises'

Title	Collective agreements for the sector 'Cleaning of buildings and premises' of Madrid (Convenio Colectivo De Limpiezas De Edificios Y Locales De Madrid)
Type of project	Collective Agreement, bulletin
Sector	Cleaning industry
Lead organisation	Dirección General de Trabajo de la Consejería de Empleo y Mujer de la Comunidad de Madrid Ilmo. Sr.:D. Javier Esteban Vallejo Santamaría. Consejería de Empleo y Mujer Código Postal: 28002, Distrito: Chamartín
Others involved	Asociación de Empresarios de Limpieza de Madrid (AELMA) Asociación Profesional de Empresas de Limpieza (ASPEL) Federación Regional de Actividades Diversas de Comisiones Obreras de Madrid.
Date of project	1 January 2005 to 31 December 2007
Contact information	Dirección General de Trabajo de la Consejería de Empleo y Mujer de la Comunidad de Madrid Ilmo. Sr.:D. Javier Esteban Vallejo Santamaría. Consejería de Empleo y Mujer Código Postal: 28002, Distrito: Chamartín

Collective agreement for the cleaning sector in Luxembourg

On 1 April 2004 a collective agreement was established between FLEN[1] and two local unions, OGBL and LCGB[2]. The purpose of the agreement is to regulate the relations, working conditions and pay of office cleaners to maintain social harmony in the sector and to battle clandestine or underground work and unfair competition between firms.

The agreement regulates working hours, night and Sunday hours and overtime, among other things. The agreement also points out the importance of equality between men and women in payment, training, professional promotion and conditions of employment. A third section directly related to working conditions is the safety and health and professional clothing section in which the obligations of employer and workers are quoted, and attention is drawn to the Act of 17 June 1994 concerning the safety and health of workers at work[3].

1 Fédération Luxembourgeoise des Entreprises de nettoyage de bâtiments.

2 Confédération Syndicale Indépendante du Luxembourg (Onofhängege Gewerkschaftsbond Lëtzebuerg) — OGBL (www.ogb-l.lu). Lëtzebuerger Chrëschtleche Gewerkschaftsbond (Fédération des syndicats chrétiens luxembourgeois) — LCGB (www.lcgb.lu).

3 Further information may be found at Legilux, Mémorial A No 016 from 2005, collective agreement 1 May 2004 for office-cleaning companies (http://www.legilux.public.lu/leg/a/archives/2005/0160102/0160102.pdf#page=16).

3.19. Anti-racism campaign (Ireland)

- The Services, Industrial, Professional and Technical Union organises campaigns against the exploitation of workers in the contract cleaning industry
- Union demands fair and proper treatment for workers
- The aim of the actions is the implementation of diversity and anti-racism policies

3.19.1. Introduction

Racism is a growing problem in Ireland as immigration levels have risen from a historically low level. After a period of inactivity, the government and the social partners are making some effort to apply anti-racism policies. The Services, Industrial, Professional and Technical Union (SIPTU), which represents workers right across the spectrum of employment in Ireland, organised a campaign against workplace racism. 'Anti-racism Workplace Week' was organised to combat the exploitation of workers in the contract cleaning sector in particular.

The Services, Industrial, Professional and Technical Union (SIPTU) represents over 200 000 Irish workers from many categories of employment across almost every sector of the Irish economy. SIPTU provides the expertise, experience and backup services necessary to assist workers in their dealings with employers, government and industrial relations institutions. In addition to its daily activities in workplace bargaining with employers, SIPTU campaigns on a wide range of issues.

3.19.2. Aims and objectives

SIPTU's objective is to organise the workers of Ireland so that they attain their full share of benefits of national wealth and economic activity in terms of living standards and equality. The union's anti-racism campaign aimed to highlight the exploitation of immigrant workers; to encourage intercultural initiatives and to support the implementation of diversity and anti-racism policies. The Anti-racism Workplace Week aimed specifically to improve the quality of life of cleaning sector workers.

3.19.3. Scope of the project — what was done

SIPTU's Anti-racism Workplace Week was held in 2001. The Union drew attention to the exploitation of workers in the contract cleaning industry and presented documented examples of contract cleaners who had been forced to work for less than the minimum wage, refused overtime for work done after hours and robbed of huge sums of money in the form of illegal deductions from their wages. In 2002 members of the SIPTU Contract Services Branch took a decision to strike to show solidarity with contract cleaning staff. In 2007 SIPTU started negotiations on a new deal for contract cleaners to guarantee them minimum pay and conditions. SIPTU was determined to end the often shameful treatment of cleaners, many of whom are migrants and vulnerable to exploitation.

3.19.4. Results and evaluation of the project

On 13 June 2007 SIPTU agreed new deal for 27 500 contract cleaners that awarded them a death-in-service benefit of EUR 5 000 and a minimum wage of EUR 9.05 per hour.

3.19.5. Details of the initiative

Table 24: Anti-racism campaign

Title	Anti-racism campaign
Type of project	Awareness and lobbying campaign
Sector	Cleaning sector
Lead organisation	The Services, Industrial, Professional and Technical Union (SIPTU) Head Office, Liberty Hall, Dublin 1, IRELAND Tel. +353 18586300, Fax +353 18749466 E-mail: info@siptu.ie
Sources of information	The Services, Industrial, Professional and Technical Union (SIPTU) website: http://www.siptu.ie/

SIMPAGS — Taking part in safety … is relevant to me (Italy) 3.20.

- Multimedia system
- Promotion of workers' participation in health and safety
- Aimed at cleaning sector

Source: http://www.uil.it/newsamb/simpags.htm

3.20.1. Introduction

According to the Istituto Nazionale Assicurazione contro gli Infortuni sul Lavoro (National Insurance Institute for Employment Injuries) — INAIL, most accidents among cleaners, in particular those with serious consequences, are caused by factors related to the work environment. Workers in city sanitation departments are particularly vulnerable to traffic accidents and need safety systems that help them minimise this risk.

Promoting workers' participation through legislation

National and EU legislation aims to promote 'workers' participation in all issues regarding health and safety'. Taking part in the system of identification, assessment and management of company risks is a right for all workers, who must be able to contribute to the protection of their own and others' health and safety. Worker participation also ensures the effectiveness and consistency of the company prevention system. However, workers' participation is still conceived in a formal way by company's experts who are responsible for prevention.

Legislative Decree 626/94 promotes 'workers' participation in all issues regarding health and safety'. Taking part in the system of identification, assessment and management of company risks is a right for all workers and ensures the effectiveness and consistency of the company prevention system. However, workers' participation may still be conceived in a formal way by company experts who are responsible for prevention.

UIL, the Italian Labour Union, developed the Simpags multimedia system to promote a culture of participation, and consequently efficient communication and relations among all the players in the prevention system. This was done in collaboration with trade unions and trade organisations from the cleaning service sector and in cooperation with a group of experts in various disciplines as well as workers themselves.

3.20.2. Aims and scope of the project

Simpags aims to promote the culture of workers' participation in safety and health in the cleaning sector. It was developed by the trade unions and trade organisations in the cleaning service sector, in cooperation with experts in various disciplines as well as workers in the sector to promote a culture of participation, and consequently efficient communication and relations among all the players in the prevention system.

The project involved a preliminary research phase and the subsequent creation of a multimedia product. During the production phase, appropriate case studies were identified, analysed and turned into films for worker instruction. The use of real workplace situations, the effectiveness of the dramatisation, and the high technical level of the films makes them both interesting and enjoyable to watch.

The Simpags multimedia project also involved the creation of:

- an instructive CD-Rom aimed at Rls (workers' safety representatives) and workers;
- a manual aimed at Rls (workers' safety representatives);
- a brochure aimed at workers.

3.20.3. Results, evaluation and transferability of the project

The Simpags multimedia project has yielded:

- a profile of the risks in the sector;
- visual reproductions of actual work situations that are easy for users to recognise themselves and, hence, easy for them to learn from;
- simple tools for the evaluation of the communication and personal relations and of each individual's working context;
- indications and suggestions for improving relations between the players in the industry, as well as improving communication to make it effective and consistent with a view to improving health and safety management in the industry.

Simpags, or a similar system, could be used in other sectors and in other countries too, although at the moment the material is in Italian only and little is available online.

3.20.4. Details of initiative

Table 25: Simpags — interactive multimedia system for participation in safety management

Title	Simpags — sistema interattivo multimediale per la partecipazione alla gestione della Sicurezza (Simpags — Interactive multimedia system for participation in safety management)
Type of project	Multidisciplinary approach to promote workers' participation in the cleaning sector. A multimedia system which provides the stakeholders with tools for improving workers' participation and analysing risks at work.
Lead organisation	UIL — uniona Italiana del Lavore
Others involved	INAIL, Italian worker's compensation authority http://www.inail.it Experts from different disciplines and workers from the sector.
Sources of information	Simpags, Pertacipare alla sicurezza … mi riguarda Internet: http://www.uil.it/newsamb/simpags.htm International film and multimedia register, International Social Security Association http://electricity.prevention.issa.int/activities/multimedia.pdf
Contact information	UIL — uniona Italiana del Lavore, Via Lucullo 6, 00187 Rome, ITALY Tel. +39 0647511 E-mail: info@uil.it http://www.uil.it

Covenant on working conditions (Netherlands) 3.21.

- Covenant on working conditions in cleaning and window cleaning sector
- Focus on occupational risks and absenteeism

3.21.1. Introduction

'Arbocovenants' are covenants on working conditions. They are drawn up between the Dutch government and the various stakeholders in each industry. Separate arbocovenants are drawn up for different sectors.

The arboconvenant for the cleaning and window cleaning sector is aimed mainly at combating certain employment risks — exposure to solvents, pressure of work, physical strain involved in lifting and actions resulting in upper limb disorders — and promoting the reintegration into work of absent cleaners during the first year of sick leave.

The covenant was drawn up by a committee (the BBC) consisting of three employee representatives, three employer representatives and three government representatives. The covenant was signed on 3 April 2003[74], by the secretary of state,

74 Arboconvenant schoonmaak- en glazenwassersbranche, 9 April 2003, Rotterdam (http://www.arbobondgenoten.nl/arbothem/arboconv/sektdoku/schoonmaak/convschoonmaak.pdf). Website Ministry of social affairs and employment, consulted on 18 July 2007, information on arboconvenants (http://www.arboconvenanten.szw.nl/index.cfm?fuseaction=dsp_dossier&set_id=1389). 'Arboconvenanten nieuwe stijl. Rapportage over de periode 1999-2002' (http://www.arbobondgenoten.nl/arbothem/arboconv/szw/convenantrapportage_1999_2002.pdf).

the employers' association for cleaning and company services (OSB), and trade unions FNV Bondgenoten and CNV BedrijvenBond.

One of the motivating factors behind the covenant was to reduce the absentee rate in the cleaning sector, which at about 10 % was very high compared with the Dutch average. Figures showed that a high number of workers from the cleaning sector also ended up claiming incapacity benefits.

3.21.2. Aims and objectives

The covenant should result in fewer workers becoming unfit for work because of their cleaning activities and in cases where disablement occurs, employer and employee should be able to work to ensure that the employee is reintegrated into work as soon as possible.

To realise this objective, quantitative objectives have been set for several safety and health related topics. Each of the objectives had to be realised by 1 July 2006. The objectives are described in the covenant[75]:

- reducing the population at risk from excessive physical strain by:
    - mapping the population at risk from excessive physical strain;
    - determining the percentage by which the population at risk has to have decreased by 1 July 2006;
- reducing the population at risk from excessive work pressure by:
    - mapping the population at risk from excessive work pressure;
    - determining the percentage by which the population at risk has to have decreased by 1 July 2006;
- reducing absenteeism by at least 20 % by 1 July 2006;
- reducing long-term absenteeism/retirement from incapacity by at least 20 % by 1 July 2006.

3.21.3. Scope of the project — what was done

Research

To give an exact picture of the health and safety situation in the cleaning sector, the BBC ordered several research studies[76]:

- Chemiewinkel Amsterdam (IVAM) studied solvents and allergenic substances;
- TNO-arbeid researched the current state of knowledge in the field of physical strain in several sectors, including window cleaning and vehicle cleaning;
- VHP advisors investigated alternatives to ladders for those who need to work at height;
- DEXIS arbeid performed a feasibility study concerning reintegration in the cleaning sector in cooperation with MarketConcern;

75 Arboconvenant schoonmaak- en glazenwassersbranche, 9 April 2003, Rotterdam.

76 Plan van aanpak Arbocovenant Schoonmaak- en Glazenwassersbranche, 9 April 2003.

- TAUW B.V. examined the state of knowledge in the field of biological agents, and developed an up-to-date protocol on their use;
- MCA Communicatie researched the topic of communication in the sector.

The measures

Based on the results from the research studies, partners were able to set specific objectives. They agreed on specific measures for the reduction of physical strain, work pressure, solvents and allergenic substances, biological agents and cytostatics.

Table 26: Important measures from the arbocovenant approach plan

Measure	Actions taken
Applying knowledge	Applying state-of-the-art knowledge in the cleaning sector, as described in the research studies Applying the basic findings of the physical strain study through a collective agreement and/or via a policy
Alleviating physical strain	Developing ergonomic aids Promoting use of ergonomic aids and materials Promoting job rotation Making agreements on the maximum exposure time in case of heavy work
Alleviating work pressure	Taking organisational and technical measures to alleviate work pressure Taking steps to rectify the discrepancy between the time required for tasks and the time available to do them
Solvents and allergenic substances	Describing and promoting healthy and safe working methods Replacing harmful products with less harmful ones
Biological agents	Setting up a protocol in each sub-sector with measures covering personal hygiene, personal protective equipment and special circumstances Getting companies whose workers are at risk from biological agents to follow the protocols
Safety and health policy, absenteeism and early reintegration	Establishing a help desk on reintegration and safety and health policy for all involved parties Promoting specific reintegration projects
Education	Developing training modules for executives: leadership coaching, handling and absenteeism, promoting reintegration and healthy working

Approach

All the measures mentioned above are discussed in detail in the plan. The overarching purpose of all these measures is to support and assist workers and employers during the treatment of occupational risks, absenteeism and reintegration on company level.

Partnerships

The most important partners in the establishment and implementation of the covenant are the organisations or institutions that signed the agreement, namely the government, represented by the secretary of state from the Ministry for Social Affairs and Employment, the employers' association OSB, FNV Bondgenotenand CNV BedrijvenBond. Other organisations and individuals were also involved, notably the research institutions mentioned above.

Finances available for the action

The Ministry for Social Affairs and Employment provided EUR 4 million, and the board for industrial relations for the cleaning and window cleaning branch (RAS) provided EUR 11 million in the name of the social partners.

Results and evaluation of the project

Orbis Advies en Onderzoek BV evaluated[77] the covenant in the first half of 2007, producing a report on its effects on working conditions and absenteeism in the cleaning and window cleaning sectors.

The report discusses the following topics: psychosocial strain, physical strain, absenteeism, knowledge and experience of employees, knowledge and experience of employers, process evaluation and costs compared to profits. The report also provides some recommendations.

Data were obtained from a questionnaire filled in by 10 000 employees from the sector, and telephone interviews conducted with 2 600 employers. The response rate among the employees was 23 % and among the employers 13 %. The results were compared with the statistics before the implementation of the covenant.

Work risks mentioned in the covenant

Employees indicated that they were more exposed to work risks during the period of the covenant than before. More workers 'often' or 'constantly' had to lift, push or carry loads of more than 25 kg than before the covenant. The risk group for physical strain remained as large as before, as did the percentage of workers performing rapid, repeated movements.

Absenteeism

The results concerning absenteeism were much better, and the goal of reducing time off was achieved. The estimated absenteeism percentage during the covenant period fell from 6.8 % in 2003 to 5.1 % in 2007, which is a decrease of 25 %. This decrease generates a saving of almost EUR 33 million a year.

Knowledge and experiences: employees

Most employees are now briefed about new tasks, have a work cupboard (locker) and have a better dialogue with their employers. However half of employees don't think they are well informed about safety and/or specific risk situations such as cleaning processes with the risk of harm caused by biological agents.

Knowledge and experiences: employers

About 90 % of the employers questioned were familiar with the covenant and 83% thought they were well informed about the covenant. One in five employers from the cleaning and window cleaning sectors who participated in the evaluation mentioned problems concerning the development and implementation of the measures from the covenant, with specific criticisms including:

- too much and too detailed information, which takes a lot of time to read and absorb;
- small companies are not specifically addressed;

77 Q.H.J.M. van Ojen, Eindevaluatie arboconvenant schoonmaak- en glazenwassersbranche, Orbis Arbeid en Onderzoek, Bussum, Augustus 2007.

- too little attention to what our clients want;
- the material is not practical enough;
- the labour inspection doesn't perform enough inspections concerning standards;
- productivity and safety are incompatible and too little attention is given to that.

Employers from the cleaning and window cleaning sector defined the success factors of the covenant. Some of them are mentioned in the evaluation report:

- the working material is of good quality, handy and practical;
- the training sessions were useful;
- the material is user-friendly and clear;
- good work support;
- respect and positive attitude towards the employee;
- RAS approached the employees in a good way;
- employers and employees decide on agreements together;
- clear communication;
- organisations are involved;
- the guiding principles are well adapted to the work in the sector.

3.21.4. Problems faced

Challenges identified with the programme were that it had too little focus — the approach plan was over-ambitious and lacked focus, which meant that several topics were not covered, and that because employers' associations and unions have different interests, it was hard to create a common starting point.

3.21.5. Success factors

The following success factors were described.

- Project management — the RAS as project organiser appeared to be a good choice. Because this organisation is closely involved with the sector it could work very effectively.
- Work groups — ad hoc or regular work groups developed the products and instruments. Both unions and organisations were represented in these groups. This enabled a practical approach and a large range of opinions.
- Diversity — the implementation of diversity in the approach and working method, the communication approach, the products and instruments made it possible to reach many different types of employers.
- Attention to employees — employees as well as employers were approached directly.

3.21.6. Details of initiative

Table 27: Covenant on working conditions in the cleaning and window cleaning branch

Title	Covenant on working conditions in the cleaning and window cleaning branch
Type of project	Covenant
Sector	Cleaning and window cleaning
Lead organisation	Ministry of Social Affairs and Employment http://home.szw.nl/index/dsp_index.cfm
Others involved	OSB (employers association; ondernemersorganisatie schoonmaak- en bedrijfsdiensten) http://www.osb.nl/ FNV Bondgenoten (trade union) http://www.fnvbondgenoten.nl/ http://www.arbobondgenoten.nl/ CNV Bedrijvenbond (trade union), http://www.cnvbedrijvenbond.nl/
Date of project	9 April 2003-1 July 2006
Sources	Plan van aanpak Arbocovenant Schoonmaak- en Glazenwassersbranche, 9 April 2003 (Approach Plan Covenant cleaning and window cleaning branch, 9 April 2003) (http://www.arbobondgenoten.nl/arbothem/arboconv/sektdoku/schoonmaak/pvaschoonmaak.pdf) Arboconvenant schoonmaak- en glazenwassersbranche, 9 April 2003, Rotterdam (Covenant on working conditions cleaning and window cleaning branch, 9 April 2003, Rotterdam) (http://www.arbobondgenoten.nl/arbothem/arboconv/sektdoku/schoonmaak/convschoonmaak.pdf) Website Ministry of Social Affairs and Employment, consulted on 18 July 2007, information on arboconvenants http://www.arboconvenanten.szw.nl/index.cfm?fuseaction=dsp_dossier&set_id=1389 Arboconvenanten nieuwe stijl. Rapportage over de periode 1999–2002 (Convenants working conditions new style. Reporting for the period 1999–2002) (http://www.arbobondgenoten.nl/arbothem/arboconv/szw/convenantrapportage_1999_2002.pdf), accessed January 2008 *Q. H.J.M. van Ojen, Eindevaluatie arboconvenant schoonmaak- en glazenwassersbranche, Orbis Arbeid en Onderzoek, Bussum, Augustus 2007* (Final evaluation of the covenant) (http://docs.minszw.nl/pdf//150/2007/150_2007_5_3683.pdf), accessed January 2008 *Arboconvenant Schoonmaaken Glazenwassersbranche. Pilot preventie verzuim vanwege psychische klachten* drs. Aukje van den Bent drs. Patricia Can met medewerking van: ir. Dorine van der Drift drs. Jos de Jonge Rapport opgesteld van de pilot die eind 2005 werd uitgevoerd in opdracht van de BBC van het Arboconvenant Schoonmaaken Glazenwassersbranche door adviseurs van BMC-SANT. Uitgave in de arboconvenantenreeks Den Haag, December 2006
Contact information	Ministry of Social Affairs and Employment (site with covenants) http://www.arboconvenanten.szw.nl/index.cfm?fuseaction=dsp_dossier&set_id=1389

Farbo subsidy for safe equipment (Netherlands)

The Dutch Ministry of Social Affairs and Employment (Ministerie van sociale zaken en werkgelegenheid — SZW) introduced the Farbo regulations to encourage entrepreneurs and non-profit organisations to invest in safe and healthy work equipment. As noise, physical strain and dangerous substances are common risks in cleaning the Farbo scheme is useful for this sector.

The ministry draws up an annual list of innovative, safe and healthy work equipment that decreases exposure to noise, physical strain or dangerous substances. Organisations that buy equipment from the list can apply for a subsidy of a maximum of 10 % of the purchase costs. The Farbo scheme not only offers financial benefits, but it also allows organisations to improve their working environment.

Examples of equipment from the Farbo list relevant to cleaning are a mobile high-pressure hot water machine for cleaning building façades without the need for dangerous chemicals, and cleaning machines that require little physical force to operate[1].

1 Further information can be found at the Agentschap website (http://agentschap.szw.nl/index.cfm?fuseaction=dsp_rubriek&rubriek_id=391294&menu_item=12868).

Promotion campaign: the cleaner makes it possible (Netherlands) 3.22.

- Promotion campaign to improve image of cleaners
- Targeted at the public and employers

3.22.1. Introduction

In 2001 Science & Strategy carried out research for the Dutch association of the cleaning industry and associated services (OSB) on the image of the cleaning sector. The target group of this study were (potential) employees. Most respondents agreed on the fact that the work is hard and dirty. Amongst cleaners themselves, the image of the cleaning sector is good, despite the staff turnover being relatively high. A large number of cleaners see the job as an entrance to the labour market. To attract enough temporary and long-term employees into the sector, it is important that cleaning has a positive image in the eyes of the public.

3.22.2. Aims and objectives

The aim was to change the public perception of cleaning work as arduous, under-appreciated and poorly paid. The campaign wanted to highlight aspects such as the variety of work, and the advances in pay in recent years in the sector. To emphasise

the social relevance of the profession, the campaign used the catchphrase 'The cleaner makes it possible'. After all, what would the world be like without cleaners [78]?

Awareness raising

The campaign will run for five years. The purpose of the first phase is to make cleaners and their jobs more visible. All target groups need to be made aware of the importance of cleaners. Promoting the sector as versatile and interesting will hopefully lead to an inflow of new workers.

Attitude

The second phase focuses on changing the attitude of clients and consumers so that they recognise the cleaner's job as important and valuable. They should value cleaners because their work contributes to their own well-being and work satisfaction.

Behaviour

The third phase of the campaign aims to achieve behavioural change among potential employees and employers.

3.22.3. Scope of the project — what was done

Several actions were taken to support the campaign: adverts in different types of media, a website and an e-magazine were created and even clothing especially designed for the cleaning sector. These and other actions are discussed in the booklet mentioned earlier.

Billboards, TV and radio commercials were used to launch the campaign in November 2002. These commercials serve two purposes: they strengthen the sense of solidarity and pride among cleaners, and portray the social relevance and interesting aspects of this dynamic working population.

The most prominent fashion designer in the Netherlands was also approached to create new industrial clothing for the cleaning sector. The result is a fresh and tailor-made design that is comfortable, functional and representative at the same time.

Anyone who is interested in any aspect of the cleaning sector and the image campaign can consult the website [79] that presents relevant, up-to-date information about and for stakeholders in the sector. The e-magazine linked to the website (Clean Magazine) provides news concerning trends and developments and is online (http://www.deschoonmakermaakthetmogelijk.nl/page.php?cat=5).

In June 2007 the campaign team started a subsidiary campaign called 'the hidden money', with the aim of persuading clients that professional, quality cleaning is worth the cost and effort, and that it pays off. There is also an online test [80] that clarifies the ways professional cleaning benefits management, and answers the question 'where is the hidden money in your company?' Visitors to the site have to answer six questions about motivated workers, what cleaners can and cannot do, about how

78 De schoonmaker maakt het mogelijk, imagocampagne, Raad voor arbeidsverhoudingen schoonmaak- en glazenwassersbranche ('The cleaner makes it possible', PR campaign, Board for industrial relations cleaning and window cleaning branch).

79 http://www.deschoonmakermaakthetmogelijk.nl/

80 http://www.hetverborgengeld.nl/

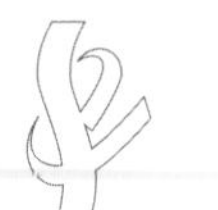

many bacteria there are on the average workstation, the importance of giving clients a good first impression, the importance of good communications and what is most irritating about a dirty work environment.

Source: extracted online 18 July 2007 (www.hetverborgengeld.nl).

After these six questions, the site provides a conclusion with the following message: 'Investing in professional cleaning has a positive influence on the company. It enhances its image, increases productivity and helps reduce absenteeism.'

In September 2007 the campaign team organised a special campaign week: The week of the cleaner. From 10 to 14 September, cleaners were put in the spotlight in all kinds of ways. Open days, recruitment drives and fun activities were organised to focus attention on the invisible activities of the cleaning sector. Cleaners were also given the chance to be nominated 'Invisible hero'. Invisible heroes are cleaners who are proud of their work and want to show this. They can participate online (http://www.onzichtbareheld.nl).

3.22.4. Details of initiative

Table 28: The cleaner makes it possible

Title	De schoonmaker maakt het mogelijk (The cleaner makes it possible)
Type of project	PR campaign cleaning sector; to convey a positive image of the cleaning sector to all its stakeholders
Sector	Cleaning sector in general
Lead organisation	RAS, Board for industrial relations cleaning and window cleaning branch, Dutch association of the cleaning industry and associated services (OSB), and the trade unions FNV Bondgenoten and CNV BedrijvenBond.
Others involved	Science & Strategy E-mail: info@science.nl
Date of project	The campaign runs over a period of five years.
Sources of information	*De schoonmaker maakt het mogelijk, imagocampagne, Raad voor arbeidsverhoudingen schoonmaak- en glazenwassersbranche* (The cleaner makes it possible, image campaign, Board for industrial relations cleaning and window cleaning branch). <http://www.schoonmaakwereld.nl> and http://www.deschoonmakermaakthetmogelijk.nl <http://www.deschoonmakermaakthetmogelijk.nl>
Contact details	E-mail: info@schoonmaakwereld.nl

3.23. Making work more pleasant: a health and safety website for cleaners and window cleaners (Netherlands)

- Information campaign on work covenant for cleaners and window cleaners
- Website provides easy access to details
- Employers and workers targeted

3.23.1. Introduction

In 2003 the social partners in the Dutch cleaning sector signed a covenant for the cleaning and window cleaning sector. Within the structure of this covenant, a website was established to inform stakeholders about all aspects of the covenant. Stakeholders can find information on the site[81] about how to reduce physical strain, exposure to dangerous products and work pressure, and how to improve support for employees who are frequently absent from work.

3.23.2. Aims and scope of the project

The objectives of the information campaign are to transfer knowledge and raise awareness of the health and safety issues for cleaners and window cleaners. The information campaign had to relate closely to the measures that were described in the covenant. The site was set up by RAS[82], with the aim of publicising the cleaning covenant. It aims to do so in a clear, informal and accessible way.

Downloads

This site allows visitors to consult information about the covenant in general and also in terms of four key occupational risks: physical strain, work pressure, dangerous products and absenteeism support. The site explains measures that can be taken to reduce these risks for different sub-sectors including office cleaning, industrial cleaning, vehicle cleaning, façade cleaning, chimney cleaning, window cleaning and cleaning in the healthcare sector. To promote and facilitate the use of these measures, RAS provides several kinds of documentation through free downloads. All the available documents and information sources are gathered in the web library, and include the following.

- 'Het Arbozakboekje — Let op je lijf!' (Health and safety pocketbook — Watch your body!) — a pocketbook describes agreements from the covenant, gives some useful tips on posture, and makes available costs and benefits models to prove the use of some of the proposed measures.
- A digital risk inventory and evaluation is available especially for the cleaning and window cleaning sector. This instrument allows employers to track down

81 Zo Werk Je Prettiger! (http://www.zowerkjeprettiger.nl/).

82 RAS: Stichting Raad voor Arbeidsverhoudingen Schoonmaak- en Glazenwassersbranche (Board for industrial relations cleaning and window cleaning sector).

occupational risks in their company and provides solutions at the same time. A demo version is available on the site and the full version can be requested freely.

Help desk

Apart from providing information, the site also provides a postal address and telephone number which can be used by workers or employers when they have questions or suggestions concerning the covenant and working conditions.

Education

RAS also provides training to help workers and employers meet the requirements of the covenant. Information about training courses is shown on the website, and interested parties can enrol online. The following training is provided:

- coaching leadership;
- preventing psychological absenteeism;
- course prevention co-worker;
- 'Stoffenmanager' cleaning — an electronic tool to keep track of the dangerous products that are used in cleaning and what one can do to prevent health damage.

3.23.3. Details of initiative

Table 29: Making work more pleasant

Title	*Zo werk je prettiger!* (Making work more pleasant!)
Type of project	Information campaign, online publication of information concerning the covenant on working conditions in cleaning and window cleaning sector
Sector	Cleaning and window cleaning
Lead organisation	The board for industrial relations in the cleaning and window cleaning branch, RAS. The management of the RAS contains representatives from the unions CNV BedrijvenBond and FNV Bondgenoten and from the employers association OSB. http://www.ras.nl/
Date of project	This initiative is directly related to the covenant and runs at the same time.
Sources of information	Website Zo werk je prettiger: http://www.zowerkjeprettiger.nl *Stichting Raad voor Arbeidsverhoudingen Schoonmaak- en Glazenwassersbranche (RAS) website: http://www.ras.nl*
Contact information	Email: info@schoonmaakwereld.nl http://www.ras.nl *Stichting Raad voor Arbeidsverhoudingen Schoonmaak-en Glazenwassersbranche* Reitseplein 1, 5037 AA Tilburg, NETHERLANDS Or: Stichting Raad voor Arbeidsverhoudingen Schoonmaak-en Glazenwassersbranche Postbus 90154, 5000 LG Tilburg, NETHERLANDS Tel. +31 135944844, Fax +31 13468 68 72 E-mail: info@ras.nl

3.24. Classifying professions (Poland)

- To identify and assess risk factors in cleaning work
- Classification criteria established for house cleaner (913102), vehicle cleaner (913211) and general cleaner (913207)

3.24.1. Introduction

Economic development brings about an increase in the number of professions and therefore international and national classifications of professions are called for. These determine the specific activities for each profession, with essential qualifications and education required. Poland's Ministry of Economics, Labour and Social Policy offers a website with information about training, job prospects and labour law covering several different professions.

3.24.2. Scope of the project — what was done

The classification is based on the International Profession Classification Standard accepted by the International Labour Statisticians Conference in Geneva in 1987 and its amended form from 1994, a so-called ISCO-88 (COM) adjusted to EU requirements. The jobs are classified according to general tasks, specialisation, skills and professional qualifications needed.

The general task of cleaning personnel is maintaining a high level of cleanliness and hygiene. Desired psychological features of a cleaning worker include: accuracy, conscientiousness, orderliness, honesty, reliability, a good sense of time and effective work organisation. The document also specifies physical requirements for a person taking up a cleaning job. General fitness is required. The contraindications for this work are: MSDs, cardiovascular diseases, respiratory system diseases and allergies. Hearing impaired persons can be employed. Educational qualifications are not relevant. Workers are employed on the basis of medical examination and an interview.

3.24.3. Results and evaluation of the project

The classification of professions was introduced in Poland because of labour market demand in accordance with the 'Act on employment promotion and labour market institutions'. The classification is a tool used in employment policy and professional counselling because it includes good practice and health and safety advice. The classification guide lets interested parties know what the possibilities of employment are, minimal professional requirements and average salary.

3.24.4. Details of initiative

Table 30: The guide to professions — II

Title	The guide to professions — II
Type of project	Guide
Lead organisation	Ministry of Economics, Labour and Social Policy — Department of Labour Market
Date of project	2003
Sources of information	Website of serwis informacyjny urzędów pracy[83] Website of Publiczne służby zatrudnienia — PSZ (Public Employment Services — PES) [84]
Contact information	Małgorzata Gołofit-Szymczak Central Institute for Labour Protection — National Research Institute/Czerniakowska 16, 00-701 Warsaw, POLAND Tel. +48 226234682/226233695 E-mail: magol@ciop.pl

Infoclean.pl Internet portal

Infoclean.pl is an Internet portal offering information relevant to the cleaning services market. The Internet portal (http://www.infoclean.pl) includes information on training, basic safety and health regulations in effect during cleaning works as well as information on disinfecting agents and sanitary regulations used during cleaning process. There is also information on cleaning in the food industry. Risk situations such as cleaning in areas subject to explosions, electrical risk and other hazards are also covered.

3.25. Polish Cleaning Association training programme (Poland)

- Polish Cleaning Association (PAC) training programme for cleaning sector workers
- Development and implementation of safety programmes for cleaning staff

3.25.1. Introduction

PAC was established in 2001, to help increase standards in the cleaning sector and raise awareness and recognition of the sector. The PAC provides basic training on occupational safety and health for cleaners. It also awards a cleaning quality mark, organises 'Cleaning Days' to publicise the profession, and jointly organises

83 http://www.praca.gov.pl/files/TOM_II.pdf?PHPSESSID=0314d77d09b09b837ffbf48b429ecf80

84 http://www.psz.praca.gov.pl/main.php?do=ShowPage&nPID=867743&pT=details&sP=CONTENT,objectID,867926 and http://www.psz.praca.gov.pl/main.php?do=ShowPage&nPID=867758&pT=details&sP=CONTENT,objectID,868220

the biannual 'INTERCLEAN Central and Eastern Europe' fair held in Warsaw. It also produces a magazine for the cleaning sector.

3.25.2. Aims and objectives

The development and implementation of safety programmes for cleaning staff seeks to raise educational standards among cleaners, enhancing the competitiveness of cleaning contractors.

3.25.3. Scope of the project — what was done

PAC training is aimed at increasing worker competence and is organised as a part of the EU initiative EQUAL and the European Social Fund. Training is divided into three levels including: operation of simple devices, use of chemical and biocidal agents, identification of hazards and rules of occupational hazards assessment, occupational safety and health management system, exceptionally dangerous work and accidents at work. PAC gives accreditation to external training companies to conduct the training on its behalf. In 2007 there were two companies accredited for this purpose in Poland.

3.25.4. Results and evaluation of the project

From 30 June 2006 to 31 July 2007 881 workers from 200 companies were trained and received certificates at first, second or third level. There was good cooperation between the cleaners and the teaching staff, and an increased availability of health and safety information for cleaners.

3.25.5. Details of initiative

Table 31: Polish Cleaning Association

Title	Polish Cleaning Association
Type of project	Education programme
Sector	Cleaning sector
Lead organisation	Polish Cleaning Association
Others involved	Marek Kowalski — president, Polish Cleaning Association 85-008 Bydgoszcz, ul. Słowackiego 1, POLAND Tel./Fax +48 523224115 E-mail: biuro@czystosc-psc.org.pl
Date of project	2001
Information sources	http://www.czystosc-psc.org.pl/
Contact information	Małgorzata Gołofit-Szymczak Central Institute for Labour Protection — National Research Institute Czerniakowska 16, 00-701 Warsaw, POLAND Tel. +48 226234682/226233695 E-mail: magol@ciop.pl

CleanNet (Finland) 3.26.

- Software to estimate time and personnel needed for cleaning tasks
- Makes the organisation of cleaning tasks easier
- Positive effect on working conditions

3.26.1. Introduction

Clean Basic Ltd is a leading multilingual working-time cost-calculating software company. Its software enables precise measuring of the time taken to perform cleaning, janitorial and catering work[85]. Aside from productivity improvements, the tool allows the allocation of enough time for a cleaner to do a proper job, avoiding the need to take risks to achieve goals, or to suffer ill health as a result of excessive work.

Based on time studies provided by the government, Clean Basic Ltd developed CleanNet, a software program that enables employers to gain an accurate idea of the staff levels, time required, likely costs and special instructions needed for their cleaning work.

After the Second World War, Finland had to pay considerable war reparations to Russia so the country made a priority of economic effectiveness and efficient time management. Every job, from forest work to assembly line was studied and timed to create time standards for different tasks.

In the 1970s the city of Helsinki began to time measure and study cleaning work in different environments using various methods. This enabled them to draw up standards that can be used in the cleaning sector. An example of such a standard is the 'method standard for damp mop'. This is a time study result for a mop 45–60 cm in size using the damp method. The standard contains eight types of information:

- the title of the standard: 'Headline Governmental cleaning method standard N:0107 floor damp mopping with a mop 45–60 cm';
- the object of the study: to time-study the mop when cleaning litter and dry dirt from the floor;
- equipment: mop 45–60 cm, extension arm 150 cm, cleaning towel 50–70 cm, floor brush and dustpan, spray can, bucket, cleaning trolley;
- cleaning agent: dust-binding or neutral cleaning agent;
- preparing and starting point: all the equipment is ready in the cleaning trolley; spray can is filled with cleaning agent and the cleaning towel is dampened with cleaning agent;
- work description: dry or pre-damped towel is placed on the mop; depending on the size of the space, the starting point is chosen so that unnecessary moving and steps can be avoided;
- cleaners can clean walking forward or backwards;

85 Clean Basic website (http://www.cleanbasic.fi).

3.26.7. Details of initiative

Table 32: CleanNet

Title	CleanNet
Type of project	Work-time measuring study
Sector	Cleaning
Lead organisation	CleanBasic, Jaakko Laiho, Management Director, Clean Basic oy Tel. +358 400676964 E-mail: jaakko.laiho@cleanbasic.fi
Date of project	CleanBasic introduced CleanNet in 2000 (ongoing)
Sources	Clean Basic http://www.cleanbasic.fi Pirjo Lehtonen, planner of cleaning work City of Helsinki Jaakko Laiho, management director Clean Basic Richard Schilling, Reutlingen University
Contact information	Jaakko Laiho, Management Director, Clean Basic Tel. +358 400676964 E-mail: jaakko.laiho@cleanbasic.fi Pirjo Lehtonen, Planner of cleaning work, Social Services Department, PO Box 7000, 00099, City of Helsinki, FINLAND Tel. +358 93104 E-mail: pirjo.lehtonen@hel.fi Dr Richard Schilling, Reutlingen University, Transportation Interior Design Alteburgstrasse 150, 72762 Reutlingen, GERMANY Tel. +49 71212718030 Mobile +49 15117205304 Fax +49 712127 1101 E-mail: richard.schilling@reutlingen-university.de

3.27. Union campaign for hotel room cleaning agreement (Sweden)

- The Swedish Hotel and Restaurant Workers Union wants hotels to sign room cleaning agreements with their cleaners
- The campaign is based on questionnaires sent to the workers and consultations held afterwards
- The eight agreements so far ask employers to specify how many rooms have to be cleaned in a given period, to reduce cleaners' workload and prevent MSDs

3.27.1. Introduction

The idea for the project came from a Hotel and Restaurant Workers Union (HRF) congress in 1996. It was felt that room cleaners have a tough work situation because of rationalisation and are thus confronted with an increasing risk of work-related injuries.

3.27.2. Aims and scope of the project

The main goal is to sign agreements with the hotel companies leading to better working conditions for the room cleaners.

The general approach is to improve working conditions and health for room cleaners at hotels by negotiation between employers and union representatives, in close cooperation with the cleaning workers themselves. The focus is mainly on measures to reduce MSDs among the cleaners.

Union staff visited more than 100 hotels in the South of Sweden. They met the room cleaners and, where appropriate, local health and safety representatives and talked to them about their working conditions, etc. They also collected the questionnaires that had previously been sent to the hotel cleaners.

The union then began negotiating with hotel management on an agreement (as an add-on to the normal labour agreements) which requires the employer to buy external expertise from the Swedish Work Health Service to prevent and tackle MSDs among cleaners. The consultants scrutinise the working environment and make recommendations on how long room cleaning should take, so that cleaners are not overworked. In addition, questionnaires were sent to 117 hotels in the South of Sweden to get information from the workers firsthand.

The agreement[88] is available in Swedish from HRF. Section 1 covers psychological as well as physical strains faced by hotel cleaners. Section 3 concerns risk assessments and Section 5 requires the employer to contract the Swedish Work Health Service or a similar institute to determine how many rooms can be cleaned in a given period.

3.27.3. Results, evaluation, and transferability of the project

The project lasted from 2003 to 2006 but HRF is in negotiations with hotel owners to sign more agreements of this type. So far, the project has generated six local room cleaning agreements. No comprehensive evaluation of the project has yet been carried out, but the union representative in charge feels that the situation of the cleaners has improved. According to HRF, the most important factor is the quality of discussions between the hotel and the union representatives. The creators of the project believe that it could be used under similar circumstances in other European countries.

88 Called Överenskommelse med förtydligande av 27 paragraph 2 mom. 'Hotellstädning' i kollektivavtalet mellan Sveriges Hotell- och Restaurangföretagare och Hotell och Restaurang Facket.

3.27.4. Details of initiative

Table 33: Room cleaning agreements

Title	Room cleaning agreements
Type of project	Labour agreement
Sector	Hotel cleaning
Lead organisation	Hotel and Restaurant Workers Union
Others involved	Hotel companies
Date of project	2003–06
Contact information	Stefan Eriksson, Hotell Och Restaurang Facket Hotel and Restaurant Workers Union Tel. +46 87810241/702470809/771575859 Fax +46 87967118 E-mail: stefan.eriksson@hrf.net http://www.hrf.net

What is workplace heath promotion? — A Swedish perspective[1], published by PREVENT Sweden, reports a 1995 project under the Alfa-Q programme (Sweden) focused on cleaning workers. The Alfa-Q programme was developed within the frame of the EU project 'Workplace Health Promotion'. It stresses the importance of psychosocial as well as physical elements of the working environment. This campaign was sponsored by Sweden's Working Life Fund.

The Alfa-Q programme focused on the cleaning industry because cleaning is an occupation regarded as having low social and economic status and offering limited opportunities for personal development. The aim of the programme was to achieve a healthier working environment for women cleaners.

The main goals of the programme were:

- greater flexibility in working hours;
- a transition to more full-time work in a sector in which part-time working used to predominate;
- a move from solitary working to group work;
- extension of job specification to include new tasks and services: so-called 'combi-services';
- the introduction of new cleaning departments with greater responsibility for finance and administration.

This programme provided cleaning staff with possibilities for learning and developing. As a result their work has become more meaningful, and influence, responsibility, occupational solidarity and job enjoyment have also increased. The overall efficiency of workers in the companies concerned has also increased, both in economic and more qualitative terms.

1 http://www.prevent.se/doc_pdf/verktyg/pdf/what_is.pdf

Qualifications for cleaners (UK) 3.28.

- British Cleaning Council supports research and education in the cleaning industry
- BCC coordinates various training activities
- One of the initiatives of BCC is promoting best practice in cleaning sector

3.28.1. Introduction

The British Cleaning Council, which represents the UK cleaning sector, was established in 1982, to promote the interests of the UK cleaning industry, and to be responsible for international relations on industry issues. The BCC has 19 members. Membership is open to any recognised trade association, research or educational body or institution concerned with industrial, commercial and institutional cleaning. The BCC coordinates many activities including research, education and training which develop and promote the interests of British cleaning workers.

3.28.2. Aims and objectives

The aim of the BCC is to coordinate the affairs of the British cleaning industry and represent the interests of all those involved. The BCC provides a forum for all members to work together to further the aims of the industry as a whole. Many of the BCC's activities support training, education and research which promote the improvement of health and safety and general standards in the working and living environment.

3.28.3. Scope of the project — what was done

One of the BCC's main tasks is to promote education within the British cleaning industry. Many of the council's 19 members organise seminars, courses and workshops which support development of occupational standards and qualifications required by the cleaning sector.

Education and training providers base their courses and workshops on the National Occupational Standards (NOS), which include descriptions of good practice in particular areas of work and offer a framework for development. National Occupational Standards detail the skills, knowledge, and understanding and occupational competences necessary to perform effectively in the workplace.

The courses for cleaning and support services are divided into five levels. Each of the steps supports achievement of new competences and qualifications.

Level 1 involves the application of knowledge and skills in the performance of a range of varied work activities, most of which may be routine or predictable. Level 2 offers competences which involve the application of knowledge and skills in a range of varied non-routine work activities, performed in a variety of work contexts. Courses on these levels are organised for building cleaning, highways and land maintenance and related sectors.

Other levels involve the application of knowledge and skills in a broad range of varied technical or professional work activities, performed in a wide and often unpredictable variety of complex or non-routine contexts. Responsibility for the work of others and the allocation of resources is often involved. Special block courses are prepared, for example for the specialised cleaning operations, fire damage limitation work, and health and safety in the workplace.

A recent initiative organised by Asset Skills, one of the members of the BCC, is a free training seminar for cleaning professionals which should support business development and improvement.

Other BCC initiatives help to overcome language barriers. The BCC supports both organisational performance and the skills development of low-paid cleaning workers and offers basic skills programmes. These learning courses deliver English language, numeracy and IT skills.

3.28.4. Results and evaluation of the project

One of the results of the BCC's activities is a rise in the number of academic institutions offering cleaning qualifications leading to degree level. The 'Qualifications for cleaners' campaign promotes professionalism and excellence within the cleaning sector.

3.28.5. Transferability of the project

The British Cleaning Council and its members provide links between employers, workers, government, agencies, small business and training providers. The campaign helps to create the educational platform which can be adapted and replicated in other sectors.

3.28.6. Details of initiative

Table 34: Qualifications for cleaners

Title	Qualifications for cleaners
Type of project	Educational campaign
Sector	Cleaning industry
Lead organisation	British Cleaning Council PO Box 1328, Kidderminster, DY11 5ZJ, UK Tel. +44 1562851129, Fax +44 1562851129 E-mail: info@britishcleaningcouncil.org
Others involved	■ Asset Skills ■ Association of Building Cleaning ■ British Association for Chemical Specialities ■ British Association for Cleaning in Higher Education (Bache) ■ British Carpet Technical Centre — Cleaning & Maintenance Research and Services Organisation ■ British Institute of Cleaning Science ■ British Toilet Association ■ Chartered Institution of Wastes Management ■ Cleaning & Hygiene Suppliers' Association ■ Cleaning and Support Services Association ■ Encams ■ Federation of Window Cleaners ■ Industrial Cleaning Machine Manufacturers` Association ■ Keep Wales Tidy ■ National Carpet Cleaners Association ■ The National Association of Wheeled Bin Washers ■ The UK Cleaning Products Industry Association ■ UK Housekeepers Association ■ Worshipful Company of Environmental Cleaners[89]

BICSc Guide to Best Value in Building Cleaning (UK)

The British Institute of Cleaning Science (BICSc) has published *A Guide to Standards, Specifications and Productivity Rates for Best Value in Building Cleaning*[1], providing cleaning standard tables, standard specifications and information on cleaning costs which ensure compliance with UK safety and health legislation. The guide recognised the need for individual specifications for sectors and buildings, including food premises, hospitals, and educational premises.

1 The British Institute of Cleaning Science, A Guide to Standards, Specifications and Productivity Rates for Best Value in Building Cleaning, 2nd edition, 2000, priced publication (http://www.bics.org.uk/).

89 Members of the BCC (http://www.britishcleaningcouncil.org/members.asp).

3.29. HSE Cleaners homepage (UK)

- The Health and Safety Executive (HSE) Cleaners homepage provides occupational health and safety advice for people working in the cleaning industry

3.29.1. Introduction

The cleaning industry employs many people in all sectors of the economy, from offices to factories, schools to hospitals, shops to aircraft. This website provides occupational health and safety advice for people working in the cleaning industry.

3.29.2. Aims and scope of the project

The purpose of the website is to provide advice and information to help improve the health and safety performance of the cleaning industry.

Identifying the main hazards in cleaning industry

The website indicates the essential hazards important to cleaning workers such as chemical and biological hazards, musculoskeletal disorders, slips and trips, and falls from height. Some topics, such as manual handling, slips and trips, falls from height, injury to back and upper limbs, and occupational dermatitis, also have their own web pages.

Providing health and safety advice and guidance for the cleaning industry

The website advertises a wide range of publications related to the cleaning sector and available from HSE Books. The publications include: free and priced guidebooks, leaflets, directives, handbooks, research reports, HSE journals and Control of Substances Hazardous to Health (COSHH) essentials guidance publications. Some publications are available in languages other than English.

Caring for cleaners: Guidance and case studies on how to prevent musculoskeletal disorders

This publication is designed for all those involved in the management of health and safety in the cleaning industry. It will be useful for employers, managers/supervisors, health and safety personnel, trainers, safety and union representatives and cleaners themselves. Guidance is provided on recognising and controlling the manual handling and upper limb risks faced by cleaners at work. A number of case studies are also provided, focusing on how organisations have reached a solution. Many of the solutions suggested are simple cost-effective measures that were developed through cooperation between supervisors, managers, safety representatives and cleaners. By applying the guidance in this book, work-related ill health and injuries suffered by cleaners can be significantly reduced [1].

1 http://www.hsebooks.com/Books/product/product.asp?catalog%5Fname=HSEBooks&category%5Fname=&product%5Fid=4280

Providing advisory services

There is an Infoline which can provide access to workplace health and safety information and expert advice (given by: phone, e-mail and published frequently asked questions (FAQs)).

Campaigns and research projects

HSE cleaners' homepage includes information about relevant campaigns and research projects, for example:

- campaigns: 'Slips and trips campaigns, Lighten the Load — 22–26 October 2007';
- research projects: Musculoskeletal health of cleaners [90], Cleaning activities and slip trip accidents in NHS acute Trusts — a scoping study (HSL 2006/08) [91].

Promotion of training and good practices

The HSE provides easy access to information on health and safety law in the form of free and priced guidebooks, videos, press releases, posters, PowerPoint presentations, publications from other organisations, training courses and seminars.

Giving statistics

The HSE cleaners' website gives statistics on work-related accidents and hazardous incidents in cleaning industry.

3.29.3. Results and evaluation of the project

The website is a source of detailed information on occupational health and safety; it helps workers become more aware of health and safety issues. Quick access is provided to further sources of information relevant to the cleaning industry.

3.29.4. Details of initiative

Table 35: HSE Cleaners homepage

Title	HSE Cleaners homepage
Type of project	Information, education
Sector	Cleaning sector
Lead organisation	Health and Safety Executive
Information sources	http://www.hse.gov.uk/cleaning/ http://www.hsebooks.com/Books/ http://www.hse.gov.uk/cleaning/guidance.htm http://www.hse.gov.uk/pubns/index.htm http://www.hse.gov.uk/contact/index.htm HSE Web Communities — Slips and Trips — 'Watch your step' ... HSE — Campaigns: Euroweek 2007 homepage http://www.hse.gov.uk/betterbacks/ http://www.hse.gov.uk/cleaning/statistics.htm

90 www.hse.gov.uk/research/crr_pdf/1999/crr99215.pdf

91 www.hse.gov.uk/research/hsl_pdf/2006/hsl0680.pdf

3.30. Cleaning Industry Liaison Forum (UK)

- In 2004 representatives of the Health and Safety Executive (HSE) and the UK's cleaning industry created a liaison forum
- The Cleaning Industry Liaison Forum (CILF) is an HSE-chaired committee that comprises representatives from the HSE, industry trade associations, trade unions and key industry stakeholders

3.30.1. Introduction

The Cleaning Industry Liaison Forum unites employers, their representative bodies, employee representatives and education and training providers, to exchange information relevant to identifying current and future health and safety issues and developing strategies to maintain and improve the industry's health and safety performance. It facilitates networking of all its members.

3.30.2. Aims and objectives

The objectives of the CILF activity are:

- to Advise the Health and Safety Executive (HSE) on health, safety, and welfare issues in the cleaning industry;
- to promote and improve the standards of health, safety, and welfare at work in the industry;
- to discuss existing and proposed legislation and how it affects the industry;
- to disseminate relevant legislation and produce guidance where necessary;
- to consider relevant guidance and information produced by other industries where this may be relevant;
- to monitor and review developments within the industry as they impact on health, safety, and welfare at work;
- to produce and agree a plan of work for 'sign-up' by the industry.

3.30.3. Scope of the project — what was done

The CILF periodically defines a strategy and plan of work for health and safety in the cleaning industry. In 2007/08 the strategy included the following topics: musculoskeletal disorders, prevention of slips and trips, prevention of falls from height, dermatitis.

UNISON, a trade union with many cleaners amongst its members, has produced a guide entitled *Caring for cleaning staff — A guide for UNISON safety representatives*. This online publication [1] is designed for UNISON safety representatives, but it can be useful for employers, managers/supervisors, and health and safety personnel. Many topics relevant to the cleaning industry are described, for example: chemical hazards, skin diseases (dermatitis), manual handling, hand-arm vibration syndrome, musculoskeletal disorders, electrical safety, personal protective equipment and clothing. The guide includes a number of case studies and instructions on how to conduct a risk assessment analysis (checklists for safety representatives are included).

1 UNISON, 'Caring for cleaning staff — A guide for UNISON safety representatives', 2000 (http://www.unison.org.uk/acrobat/11192.pdf).

3.30.4. Results and evaluation of the project

CILF is an important forum for exchanging information between employers, trade associations, trade unions, manufacturers and those using cleaning services. It keeps the users of cleaning services abreast with standards for professional cleaning and helps them understand their obligations to employees and customers.

CILF's educational and research activity shows employers that, by investing in the skills of their staff, they are investing in their business. The forum helps workers become more aware of the health and safety issues that affect them, as well as their responsibilities, so they can play their part in improving health and safety in the workplace. An increased awareness among cleaning workers leads to a lower accident rate and improves the quality of work.

3.30.5. Details of initiative

Table 36: Cleaning Industry Liaison Forum

Title	Cleaning Industry Liaison Forum
Type of project	Forum
Sector	Education, information
Date of project	2004
Information sources	Health and Safety Executive (HSE) website Members of the Cleaning Industry Liaison Forum — Strategy Group http://www.hse.gov.uk/cleaning/forum.htm See also Asset Skills — the Sector Skills Council for the Property, Facilities Management, Housing and Cleaning industries http://www.assetskills.org/site/ Association of Building Cleaning Direct Service Providers http://www.abcdsp.org.uk/ British Cleaning Council (BCC) http://www.britishcleaningcouncil.org/members.asp British Institute of Cleaning Science (BICS) http://www.bics.org.uk/ Chartered Institute of Environmental Health (CIEH) http://www.cieh.org Cleaning and Support Services Association (CSSA) http://www.cleaningindustry.org/cssa_home.asp Darin Clayton (UK) Ltd http://www.darwinclayton.co.uk Federation of Window Cleaners http://www.nfmwgc.com GMB http://www.gmb.org.uk Local Authorities Coordinators of Regulatory Services (LACORS) http://www.lacors.gov.uk/lacors/home.aspx Industrial Cleaning Machine Manufacturers' Association http://www.icmma.org.uk/ One Complete Solution (OCS) Ltd http://www.OCS.co.uk/ The Worshipful Company of Environmental Cleaners http://www.environmental-cleaners.com/ Transport and General Workers Union TGWU http://www.tgwu.org.uk/ UK Housekeepers Association http://www.ukha.co.uk/ Unison — the trade union for people delivering public services http://www.unison.org.uk/ Indepth Hygiene Services Limited http://www.indepthhygiene.co.uk/

Building Cleanability Awards (UK) 3.31.

- Established in 1995 by the Worshipful Company of Environmental Cleaners, a City of London Livery Company
- A biennial competition, whereby a team of assessors visit nominated buildings and evaluate their 'cleanability', i.e. the relationship between the building's design, material usage and day to day cleaning effectiveness

3.31.1. Introduction

The Building Cleanability Awards set out to promote better design of buildings from the moment an architect receives a commission. The awards identify 76 key features of a building which contribute to its ease of cleaning with many of these features closely associated with issues of Health and Safety.

3.31.2. Aims and Objectives

- The Building Cleanability Awards set out to establish a close working relationship between those responsible for the design of buildings and those responsible for the maintenance, cleaning and safe working procedures of a building once occupied.
- To develop guides of good practice within the architectural profession which allow issues of health and safety and ease of cleaning the building environment to be identified and designed into the building from its design concept.
- To encourage a better working environment through the incorporation of features of good practice into the overall design of a building.
- To create a working liaison between the architectural profession and all elements of the cleaning industry fully inclusive of agencies such as Health and Safety.
- To promote awareness of the cleaning needs and 'cleanability' issues relevant to all public and commercial buildings, at all stages of design/construction and operational management.

3.31.3. Scope of the project

The project sought to give recognition of good 'cleanability' design by way of a prestigious awards ceremony in the City of London, at the completion of each biennial scheme, together with a star grading system for all participants. Assessment criteria are subject to annual review so that they incorporate current good practice. In addition, the project seeks to develop, through working parties, an effective dialogue with architects to ensure that best practice takes account of cleanability and health and safety issues.

3.31.4. Results and evaluation

In August 2008, a dialogue was established with the Royal Institute of British Architects which will lead to the establishment of a joint cleaning industry/architectural profession working party to take the project forward. The ultimate goal is that all new building or refurbishment projects undergo a 'cleanability' audit, prior to the commencement of building work, similar to that pertaining for health and safety issues.

3.31.5. Details of initiative

Table 37: Cleaning Industry Liaison Forum

Title	Cleaning Industry Liaison Forum
Type of project	Competition
Sector	Cleaning, construction, design
Date of project	Since 1995
Information Source	Building Cleanability Awards http://www.cleanabilityawards.co.uk/

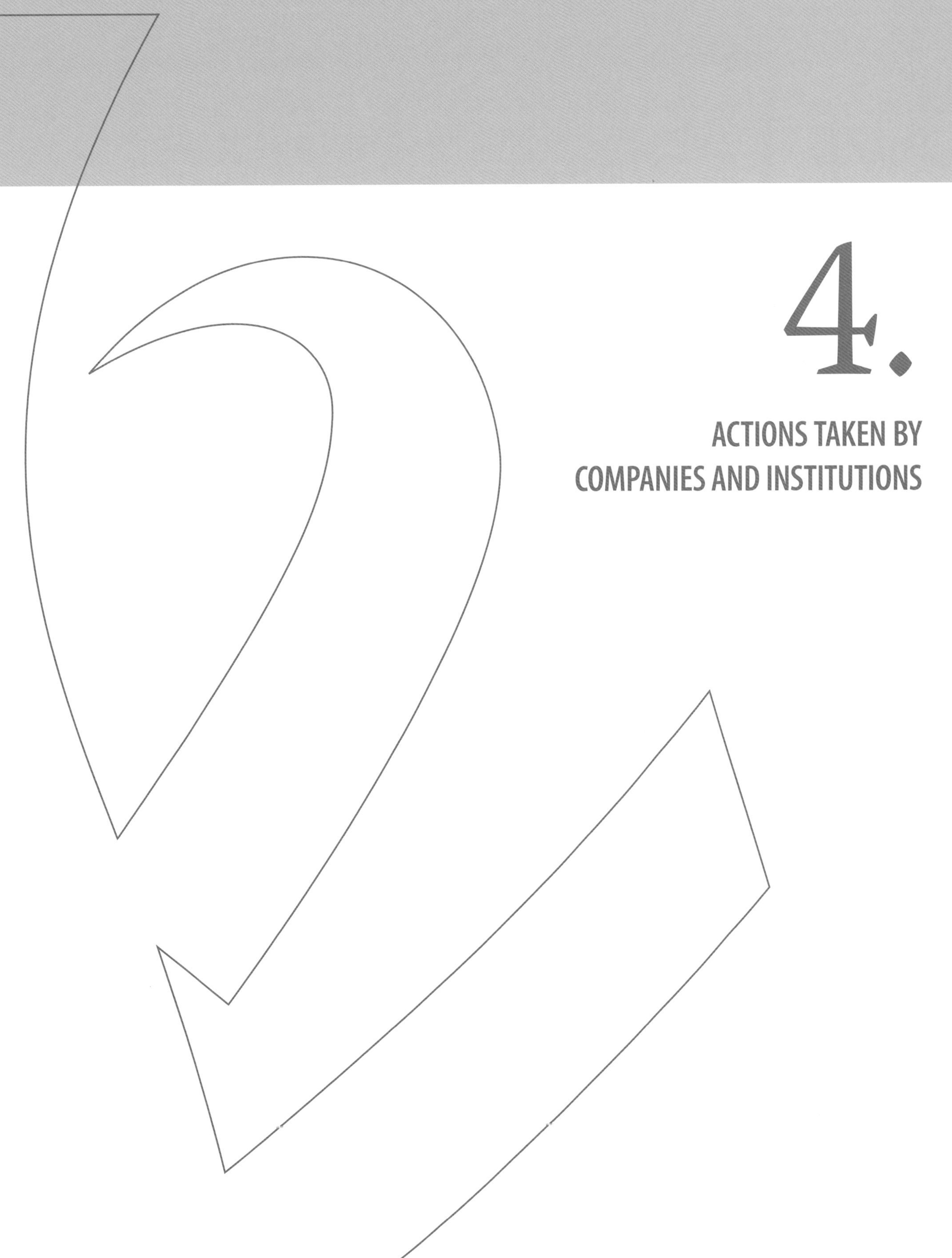

4.

ACTIONS TAKEN BY COMPANIES AND INSTITUTIONS

As with the examples in the previous chapter, the cases presented here are samples from across Europe, illustrating the range of interventions possible to reduce the risks to cleaning workers' safety and health. The cases have been structured to improve accessibility, and where the data exists give the costs and benefits involved.

4.1. 'Toolbox' meetings help create a safer workplace — CARE NV (Belgium)

- Short 'toolbox' meetings held to increase workers' safety awareness
- Resultant decrease in occupational accidents

4.1.1. Introduction

CARE NV was founded in 1974. With over 1 000 employees it is one of the 10 largest cleaning service companies in Belgium. CARE offers different types of cleaning services, including office and industrial cleaning. About 70 % of the employees are women and about 28 % are immigrants comprising around 32 different nationalities.

In 2005 CARE entered the 'Best Employer in Belgium' contest for the first time. The company won a special award for diversity and was named the seventh best employer in the country. In 2006 the company came sixth. This contest is organised within the framework of the Great Place to Work Institute, which publishes lists of the best employers in over 30 countries all over the world[92].

With this track record, it is evident that CARE is committed to its employees and concerned about their well-being. In fulfilling this commitment CARE has to overcome several negative factors endemic to the cleaning industry — including a heavy workload, high number of occupational accidents and lack of autonomy on the part of workers.

Based on both its responsibility towards its employees and the need to reduce the costs associated with occupational accidents, CARE decided to analyse the situation to find the causes behind the high accident rates.

An analysis of the occupational accidents revealed that employees had the habit of stopping work to visit the doctor after every minor incident at work. This resulted in a high absenteeism rate, even though many of these incidents were insignificant. The analysis also revealed that about 43 % of accident victims were workers with less than one year's service and about 32 % of the victims had been in service for less than a month.

The high absentee rate came about partly because of misconceptions on the part of workers about occupational accidents and their consequences. Many employees believed that if they had an accident at work, in order to establish that it was an occupational accident they needed to see the doctor immediately and then go home.

92 http://www.greatplacetowork-europe.com

In the past CARE had implemented some safety strategies that could be used in this project too. In 2005 for example, they implemented toolbox meetings to tackle unsafe situations on site. Toolbox meetings are short on-site meetings between the leader and his/her team where the team leader or the prevention advisor discusses an actual safety topic to point out dangerous situations and raise the workers' awareness of how to deal with them.

4.1.2. Aims and objectives

The objectives of the project were the following.

- Eliminating misconceptions about the procedure concerning occupational accidents: to make sure every employee understands the meaning and consequences of an occupational accident. What is an occupational accident? What does an employee have to do when they have an accident?
- Enhancing feelings of safety: to make sure that employees feel safe during work because this can result in a lower staff turnover and more respect for the company (they care about us).
- Decreasing the number of occupational accidents: to identify pseudo-occupational accidents and inform workers about working safely. CARE aimed to reduce the number of accidents by 10 % in 2007 compared to 2006.

4.1.3. Scope of the project — what was done

In January 2007 the company's occupational safety committee met to discuss ways of reducing the high accident and absenteeism rate. They decided to use the toolbox meetings to raise employee awareness and explain the procedures to be taken in the event of an occupational accident. One toolbox focused specifically on the reporting of accidents, explaining the different steps to be taken in the case of a 'serious' accident as well as a minor one.

Table 38: Take Care Meeting

TAKE CARE MEETING	
LOCATION:	DATE:
Reporting occupational accidents No matter how careful we are, accidents do happen and you may find yourself the victim of an accident at work. What you do next is: If the accident is not serious, let your supervisor know immediately. Tell them what happened to you. It's not necessary to consult the doctor immediately. Your supervisor will record the accident. If, after some time, you seem to be fine and you can carry on work as usual we will classify the accident. If you do not feel well, you can still consult a doctor who will provide you with the necessary care. Thus, to make sure your incident will be recognised as an occupational accident, you only have to inform your supervisor. If something happens at home (e.g. slipping during cleaning), we don't run immediately to the doctor. In CARE it is no different. In case of a serious accident, you also immediately inform your supervisor and you visit the doctor. Don't forget to get the doctor to fill in all the necessary documents. These documents have to be posted as soon as possible to CARE accompanied by your certificate of absence. Your supervisor will answer any questions you may have.	
Trainer	
NAME of EMPLOYEE	SIGNATURE

Form covering a toolbox meeting on 'Reporting occupational accidents'.

Other themes are covered in these toolbox meetings, including the following.

- 'Wearing the right shoes at work.' An explanation of what kind of shoes have to be worn for what kind of work.
- 'What does the label mean?' This toolbox explains the meaning of various safety labels such as corrosive substance, explosive substance, emergency exit, etc.
- 'Don't stumble'. This toolbox reminds employees to be careful and watch out where they walk.
- 'Engage brain before action'. This is an ergonomic toolbox.

When a new employee is hired, he or she has to follow all existing toolbox meetings, which are led by the team leaders or the prevention officer (the first time). Team leaders receive training from the prevention advisor on how to conduct a toolbox meeting.

Organisation chart

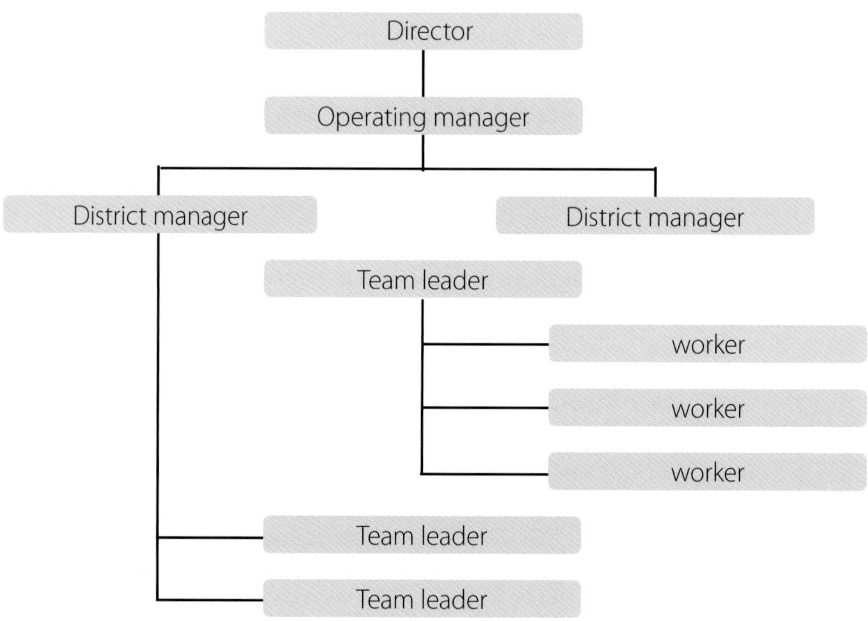

Other initiatives taken to enhance safety awareness include the following.

- A monthly safety slogan is printed on the payslip, which relates to the toolbox that was given in that period. In January 2007, for example, the following slogan was 'Say no to occupational accidents! We wish you all a safe 2007.'
- Every quarter special attention is given to a safety topic in the staff newsletter.
- An additional newsletter is published concerning safety (for all employees).

4.1.4. Results and evaluation of the project

Workers are wearing safety shoes, and both employees and managers have an increased safety awareness. Safety measures are no longer seen as a burden, but are carried out as a matter of course. As a result, fewer accidents happened.

Thanks to the toolbox meetings, there is more clarity amongst the employees about the procedures concerning occupational accidents. Some employees who had an accident remained at work after they had reported it because their injuries were minimal. Workers are no longer worried that if their injury gets worse the incident will not be recognised as an occupational accident. As CARE only began the project in January 2007, it is too soon to have quantitative results.

4.1.5. Problems faced

Paying attention to the prevention of occupational accidents is important but it can also generate side effects. Once their attention has been drawn to occupational accidents, workers might take advantage of this. For example, students who never heard of occupational accidents before might see the procedure as an easy way to avoid work by filling in an accident declaration. However, the extensiveness of the declaration procedure now deters false claimants.

4.1.6. Success factors

The employees of cleaning contractors usually work at different workplaces with different types of risk factors. This presents a challenge for the prevention officer, not least because it is difficult to contact all employees easily as they are at different locations. The idea of toolbox meetings was a good way of meeting this challenge. The toolbox meetings give team leaders the chance to inform and educate employees in a practical setting.

4.1.7. Transferability of the project

Toolbox meetings can be used in all kinds of organisations from different sectors. These meetings are easy to organise and do not take too much time. The informal workplace setting makes it much more accessible for workers than theoretical training sessions.

4.1.8. Details of initiative

Table 39: Toolbox meeting as a means to create a safer work environment at CARE NV

Title	Toolbox meetings as a means to create a safer work environment at CARE NV
Type of project	Worker participation, enhancing worker engagement, reducing accidents
Focus	Cleaning and facility sector (several services)
Lead organisation	CARE NV
Contact person	CARE NV Els Van Rijckeghem, prevention officer Luchthavenlei 7B bus 2, 2100 Deurne, BELGIUM Tel. +32 70233187 E-mail: els.van.rijckeghem@care.be http://www.care.be
Date of project	Toolbox meetings started in 2005 Project focusing on occupational accidents started January 2007

4.2. AMS BAU — Occupational safety and health policy for cleaning workers in AVANT-Gebäudedienste GMBH (Germany)

- Promoting health and safety among cleaners of buildings
- Non-mandatory certification, enabling cost to be kept down
- Motivation through good information
- Predictability of legal decisions
- Publicity effects concerning clients

4.2.1. Introduction

At the beginning of the 1990s the increasing demands of customers for fault-free technology and high-quality products led to the proliferation of quality management systems. In the meantime quality management based on standards DIN EN ISO 9000 ff. has found application in many stationary industries. The certification of management systems is associated with considerable costs.

Quality management systems and many of the occupational health and safety management systems commonly used in Germany are designed to meet the needs of stationary industries. The requirements of the building industry with its difficult conditions, such as constantly changing workplaces, weather conditions or specific contractual forms, were largely ignored. In addition, an ever increasing number of customers make high demands of the occupational health and safety provisions of their contractors.

Within the framework of a pilot project the Berufsgenossenschaft der Bauwirtschaft — BG BAU (Institute for Statutory Accident Insurance and Prevention of the Building Industry) developed an occupational health and safety management system that would exert a positive influence on existing quality management systems. The primary subject of the study was the operating procedures relating to personnel, finance and organisation. On the basis of the results, solutions were developed which were meant to integrate occupational health and safety into the existing organisational structures of small and medium-sized enterprises in the building industry; that is, those with fewer than 50 employees. Given the specific nature of the building industry it was important that occupational health and safety did not raise new bureaucratic hurdles but that the issues behind occupational health and safety were systematically integrated in decision-making processes and in the running of the organisation.

In the course of this pilot project, which was funded by the then Federal Ministry of Economics and Labour, an action plan with corresponding implementation aids was developed in cooperation with the Zentralverband des Deutschen Baugewerbes (National Association of German Builders — ZDB).

The application and implementation of the AMS BAU action plan is based on voluntary participation and offers companies the opportunity to establish an occupational health and safety organisation. The AMS BAU is not subject to mandatory certification and thus offers a cost-effective alternative.

There are many reasons for establishing an occupational health and safety policy. Apart from the promotion of health and safety, the operational and financial aspect also plays an important role. This includes, for instance, fewer working days lost due to work-related illness or accidents and increased staff motivation.

The action plan is divided into 11 consecutive stages to be followed through in chronological order. The reader is given an explanation for each stage and information on the approach and documentation (implementation aids are included in the annex) and finally a 'to do' list where they can enter which tasks have to be completed.

Table 40: AMS BAU — 11 stages towards safe and economic building and cleaning work

	AMS BAU — 11 stages towards safe and economic building and cleaning work
1	Preparation of an occupational health and safety policy
2	Setting of targets
3	Definition of organisational structures and areas of responsibility
4	Coordination of information flow and cooperation, and identification of statutory and other requirements
5	Identification and assessment of risks, preparation and implementation of corresponding measures, control
6	Arrangements for breakdowns and emergencies
7	Procurement
8	Selection of and cooperation with subcontractors
9	Preventive occupational medicine measures
10	Qualification and training
11	Result verification of objectives, verification of labour organisation

The 11 stages are based on the German guideline for occupational health and safety management systems (NLF). The term occupational health and safety management system (Arbeitsschutz-Managementsystem AMS) refers to all organisational measures within a system that contribute to the improvement in occupational health and safety, the prevention of accidents and the promotion of health. One aim of the AMS BAU is to offer small and medium-sized companies in the building industry the opportunity to meet the legal requirements for an occupational health and safety management system. The AMS BAU caters to the operational (personnel and financial) requirements of SMEs in the building industry. Discussions with potential customers showed that the AMS BAU is given the same status among SMEs as other occupational health and safety management systems. At the same time the appraisal in accordance with AMS BAU demonstrates that the requirements of OHSAS 18001 have been met.

With the introduction and implementation of an effective occupational health and safety organisation responsible companies demonstrate to their staff that occupational health and safety is a business objective. Apart from the legal certainty achieved by the implementation of the AMS BAU, because over 80 % of the above mentioned stages are based on statutory requirements, the implementation of an effective occupational health and safety policy also leads to an improvement in operational communication and information flow. Greater transparency improves workflows and ultimately also the company's image. The AMS BAU model therefore represents a wide-ranging approach to the improvement of occupational health and safety.

The AVANT Gebäudedienste GmbH cleaning company, which employs about 400 cleaners, had carried out a great deal of activity in the past to achieve management quality certification. So AVANT was accredited DIN-EN-ISO 9001:2000 in the year 2005. Nevertheless, the management wanted to ensure that improvement was continuous. It was felt that there could be greater coordination and efficiency in the working methods of the cleaning groups. Discussions with an external safety and health expert resulted in a series of problems to be tackled. For example, different cleaning supplies were used for the same cleaning jobs; the maintenance and servicing of machinery was not well organised; too many chemicals were used in general. AVANT therefore chose the AMS BAU system, because of its ease of implementation, low cost and high standard.

4.2.2. Aims and objectives

The most important aim is to avoid occupational accidents and diseases. There is also a monetary gain through fewer work days lost to illness, better organisation, more economical purchasing and less damage to machinery.

4.2.3. Scope of the project — what was done

Launching AMS BAU took about a year and it was finished in the middle of 2006. The most important implemented activities were the choice and training of safety representatives, the designation of certain rooms as central information points, and the organisation of regular health and safety meetings. Each area manager was allocated a fund to purchase necessary safety equipment without delay.

Table 41: Project targets and the steps to achieve them

Target	Measure	Responsible	When
Reducing accidents	Continuous education	Area manager, senior workers	Continuously
	Regular instruction, plus special instructions on new tasks, machinery or chemicals		Before machinery or chemicals are put into use
	Special action concerning skin protection	Management with company doctor and safety engineer	According to catalogue of measures
Reducing absenteeism	Prevention of health (skin protection, back school, flu shot)	Management with company doctor	According to catalogue of measures
	Continuous analysis	Management with doctor and area manager	According to catalogue of measures
Improving communication	Daily meetings before work start — positive/negative situations	Management with doctor and area manager area manager, safety engineer	Daily
	Short meetings concerning special cases of safety representatives	Safety engineer activated by the management	Every three months
Legal compliance	Clear assignment of tasks, responsible activities, authority	Manager	According to catalogue of measures for the current year

4.2.4. Results and evaluation of the project

The company's actions in improving health and safety made the workers feel safer and improved their levels of motivation. The workers' feeling is: 'my boss cares about me'. They began to use their personal protective equipment as a matter of course, without being prompted. Through greater safety measures, regular maintenance checks and better exchange of information the safety record in using machinery is high.

There have been two tangible economic advantages: only one type of vacuum cleaner is now used, making servicing easier and the number of chemicals used has been drastically reduced — these can now be bought in large quantities at a reduced price.

4.2.5. Details of initiative

Table 42: AMS BAU — OSH and health management policy for cleaning workers in AVANT

Title	AMS BAU — Occupational safety and health management policy for cleaning workers in AVANT Gebäudedienste GMBH
Type of project	Introducing and implementing an occupational safety and health management system for cleaners
Focus	Integration of occupational safety and health into the organisational structures of small and medium-sized enterprises in the building and cleaning industry
Lead organisation	AVANT Gebäudedienste GMBH
Contact person	AVANT Gebäudedienste GMBH Reiner Nonn, Director Rudolfstraße 55, 99092 Erfurt, GERMANY Tel. +49 3616726210, Fax +49 3616726219 E-mail: kontakt@avant-gebaeudedienste.de
Other organisation(s) involved	Berufsgenossenschaft der Bauwirtschaft — BG BAU (Institute for Statutory Accident Insurance and Prevention of the Building Industry — BG BAU)
Other partners	External safety engineer; company doctor

4.3. Introducing a health circle in a cleaning service (Germany)

- Increasing illness among cleaners at clinic led to the formation of a 'Health circle' with the participation of management and personnel department
- Cleaners were equipped with new work clothes
- Cleaners were encouraged to do physical exercise, relaxation exercises
- A fitness brochure was developed
- Absenteeism was tackled holistically

4.3.1. Introduction

An increase in the incidence of ill health among the 100 or so cleaners at the Dr Horst-Schmidt Clinic led to the implementation of a Gesundheitszirkel Reinigungsdienst (Health circle (or forum) for the cleaning service) in 1999. The health circle was embedded in a tradition of health promotion in this hospital going back more than 12 years, and it attempted to integrate methods and goals of occupational safety and health with those of health promotion and personnel management.

A series of measures were developed (e.g. training in ergonomic cleaning techniques, fitness and relaxation exercises, and discussions about absence from work). Some of the measures served as an immediate intervention. Beyond that, a strategy for sustainability was developed for the more long-term concerns of the health circle. One element of this strategy was a fitness brochure with a cleaner as the photo model. To evaluate the whole process a questionnaire was given to the participating cleaning workers before and after implementation of the measures. In the meantime, the cleaning service health circle serves as a model for other problem areas in the company.

In the late 1990s the clinic faced three main problems with its cleaning service:

- in just two years ill health among cleaners had increased significantly; these health problems were mentioned by cleaners during occupational medical examinations and workplace inspections and reported by the management;
- the already high percentage of lost time due to illness nearly doubled from 9.6 % to 18.7 % in a single year;
- at the same time, the standard of cleaning was sometimes inadequate, causing concern among patients.

The 1 000-bed hospital employed about 100 permanent cleaners. During the previous three years they had been subject to restructuring measures aimed at improving productivity in comparison with external cleaning services. The restructuring had involved a reduction in staff. Hence, each employee had larger areas to clean and was required to carry out more overtime. At the same time the long-time head of the cleaning service retired. The absentee rates in the cleaning service of this hospital were considerably higher than, for example, the Bavarian civil service, which had a rate of 7.9 % in 1999[93].

Working time lost to illness depends not only on the worker's objective physical health, but on other factors such as leadership behaviour, job recognition and working environment. Complicated additional burdens, in particular the double load of employed mothers, and motivation problems caused by a lack of appreciation, seem to play a special role. The social backgrounds of the employees are also relevant.

4.3.2. Aims and objectives

The goals of the initiative were to reduce lost time, and to improve the self-esteem and job satisfaction of the cleaners. The intention was to focus on acute problems first, and, when these were in hand, to ensure the sustainability of the programme by implementing lasting measures and activities.

93 Bayerischer Staatsminister der Finanzen: Fehlzeiten der Beschäftigten des Freistaats Bayern 2000. pp. 1-24 (http://www.bayern.de/stmf/seiten/blick/fehlz.pdf (no longer available on the internet)).

4.3.3. Scope of the project — what was done

In the health circle, particular importance was attached to the statements of the cleaning workers about possible loads and stresses.

The situation was analysed and a list of stressors drawn up. Ergonomic deficiencies were considered to be the greatest problem, e.g. non-ergonomic movements and having to use mops and brooms whose handles were far too long. A lack of appreciation of the cleaners' work, heavy workload, a high average age and long service duration were also factors.

Within four weeks the first measures were put into place. The cleaners were issued with new, smart trousers suits to replace their old smocks. Reports in the clinic newsletter about tasks and problems of the cleaning service improved the motivation of the cleaning service employees.

In the medium term, all cleaners were given training in small groups by the personnel and medical departments. Some of the main topics were ergonomic work technologies and the development of body awareness so that cleaners would consciously adopt more comfortable and healthy postures. The training was complemented with instruction on fitness exercises and relaxation practices.

Employees who frequently took sick leave were interviewed in detail by the personnel department. Individual support was offered in the case of social problems.

After the training courses a fitness brochure was developed to encourage the cleaners to continue the fitness and relaxation exercises. The brochure used clear illustrations with brief text. About nine months after completion of the training courses further training was carried out in larger groups, and attended by most of the cleaners.

4.3.4. Results and evaluation of the project

The results of the health circle were evaluated by comparing two questionnaires distributed at the beginning and at the end of the health circle. The first questionnaire showed a high prevalence of MSDs and that the average age of the interviewees was about 45 years (25 % were over 50). About half of the predominantly female cleaners were looking after two or more children in addition to their household. The cleaning of toilets, of showers and vertical surfaces stressed the workers. Ergonomic deficiencies in both cleaning methods and equipment were frequently mentioned. Adjustable aluminium telescopic handles were purchased to solve this problem. The cleaners also felt there was too much time pressure on them. Because of a high rate of absenteeism and staff cutbacks, the cleaners hardly ever found themselves working in the same area, but were moved frequently around the clinic.

The evaluation of the second set of questionnaires indicated that there was a high acceptance of the health circle among cleaners. Among the interviewees, 85 % approved of the measures taken. The most popular was the introduction of the new uniform (71 %), followed by the new working shoes (35 %), the new cleaning techniques (31 %) and the fitness and relaxation exercises and fitness brochure (26 %). The new cleaning techniques could be employed by 81 % of the workforce.

While 41 % of the cleaners said their health complaints had not improved since the start of the action, the rate of MSDs dropped, with almost 60 % of sufferers reporting less pain.

Further changes or improvement measures were desired, e.g. improved ergonomic working devices and changed working hours with improved rests as well as the regular offer of gymnastics. The percentage of lost time due to illness dropped to 10 % with a trend to more improvement. The action can be considered a success. Long-term effects such as improved health awareness can be expected.

4.3.5. Problems faced

At the beginning of the health circle it was decided not to interview all of the cleaners because of time pressures and because some of them did not speak German well. During the small group-training sessions, a questionnaire had to be filled out by the participants, some of whom required assistance to do so. There was also unexpected resistance among some of the older cleaners to the introduction of the trouser suits, but once they had been introduced there was general acceptance.

4.3.6. Success factors

A success factor of this project was that from the beginning management was included to enable decisions to be made quickly and implemented effectively.

The health circle was embedded in a tradition of health promotion in the hospital that has lasted for over 12 years. Apart from immediate interventions, a strategy of sustainability was developed to ensure that solutions implemented would have long-term effects. One measure of this strategy, a fitness brochure using a cleaning worker as model, was evaluated very positively by the employees.

Industrial safety and health protection, health promotion and personnel management were all involved in this health circle, which meant it came up with holistic solutions that addressed problems from all angles rather than focusing on one aspect only. This was a success factor because there is often little communication and cooperation between these groups.

During the programme the attitude of the cleaners towards health matters changed and some of them even changed their private health behaviour. Interest in other measures of the health promotion, for example smoking cessation, increased.

4.3.7. Transferability of the project

The methodology of this health circle could easily be transferred to other hospitals or companies with similar problems. It could also be implemented in other sectors. If the management recognises the opportunities resulting from such a circle, it can be a powerful means of preventing occupational illness and absenteeism. The health circle can be used as a preventive measure, in the event that there is pressure to start interventions immediately.

4.3.8. Details of initiative

Table 43: Health circle cleaning services

Title	Gesundheitszirkel Reinigungsdienst (Health circle cleaning services)
Type of project	Health circle, interventions, brochure, training
Focus	Hospital cleaning workers, ergonomics, ill health reduction
Lead organisation	Dr Horst-Schmidt-Kliniken GmbH
Contact person	Dr med. Thomas Weber Dr med. Vera Stich-Kreitner Personalärztliche Abteilung Ludwig-Ehrhard-Str 100, 65199 Wiesbaden, GERMANY E-mail: thomas.weber@hsk-wiesbaden.de vera.stich-kreitner@hsk-wiesbaden.de
Other partners	External safety engineer; occupational medicine
Date of project	1999–2001/02

Getting workers involved in analysing risks: an example of hospital cleaners (Germany)

The general aim of this project at a Hanover hospital was to implement an occupational safety and health management system to cover not only the medical staff but also all support services. The work was led by health forums in each of the various hospital services which were able to identify specific risks and target groups at the workplace concerned and to elaborate adequate measures.

A steering committee was formed, including representatives of all categories of hospital staff and management. The steering committee developed an overall implementation and information strategy, consisting of 10 steps (including anonymous worker surveys in order to identify special strains, health risks and possible sources of accidents, implementation of health forums in the various services, identifying concrete measures and proposing them to the steering committee, etc.).

One health forum was formed by the cleaning workers of the hospital, all of them women. This forum was originally supposed to discuss working postures, wet work, and the risks posed by chemical disinfectants. But it became obvious that psychological rather than physical risks were the main concern of the cleaning staff.

The cleaners suffered from disrespect regarding their work and from sexual harassment from colleagues as well as patients. The impractical work uniform — a short dress made of synthetic fabric — was identified as the main reason for sexual harassment and further risks.

- Especially when cleaning floors and stairs or when bending forward the women felt exposed to their male colleagues and patients.
- The synthetic fabric of the dress increased perspiration, which made the workers feel very uncomfortable.
- The design and cut of the dress was a point of discussion: it tended to get caught on work equipment, door handles and handrails. This was considered dangerous in that it could easily lead to accidents at work.

The health forum reported to the steering committee and tested new uniforms consisting of a cotton tunic and trousers. This new outfit not only cut down the number of suggestive remarks directed at the cleaners, but it also corresponded more closely to the design of the nurses' clothing. Wearing the new clothes made the staff feel as if they had been upgraded to the medical and caring staff.

As a result the job satisfaction and the self-confidence of the workers were enhanced, and several risk factors for the job eliminated. The project also had the added effect of sensitising the workers to safety and health issues.

Contact information
Dr Frank Wattendorff
Leibniz Universität Hannover
Weiterbildungsstudium Arbeitswissenschaft (WA)
Schloßwender Str. 5
30159 Hannover, GERMANY
Tel. +49 5117625979
Fax +49 5117623966
E-mail: frank.wattendorff@wa.uni-hannover.de
http://www.wa.uni-hannover.de
Doris Pelstring
Klinikum Hannover Siloah
Roesebeckstr. 15
30449 Hannover, GERMANY
Tel. +49 51192726 51
http://www.klinikum-hannover.de
Further information
Initiative Neue Qualität der Arbeit (INQA) website http://www.inqa.de

EU-OSHA — European Agency for Safety and Health at Work, Diversity in Risk Assessment (not yet published)

4.4. Enabling people with disabilities to work as cleaners (Germany)

- People with mental disabilities can carry out cleaning activities
- Strongly structured work routines assist in career success and further development
- Consultation by specialised companies increases safety at work
- Cleaning services employing people with disabilities can compete strongly in the market

4.4.1. Introduction

Like everyone else, people with disabilities have the right to personal development. Participating in working life opens up possibilities for self actualisation, independence

and personal recognition. This case study gives two examples of people with mental disabilities being integrated into working life as building cleaners.

The care of the employees is carried out by two welfare services, the Diakonie-Werkstätten Berlin gGmbH, Werkstatt Weißensee (Diakonie workshops of Berlin gGmbH, workshop Weissensee) and the Märkisch-Oderland Werkstätten Lebenshilfe e.V. — MOL (Märkisch-Oderland workshops life assistance e.V. — MOL). These facilities cooperate with a company that gives technical support. The cleaning services are offered on the free market under competitive conditions. MOL, founded in 1990, is a self-help union of parents with mentally handicapped children. Its workshop employs and trains about 240 mentally handicapped people.

Workshops for people with mental disabilities have to fulfil a dual task. Not only does the work have to be appropriate for the level of ability and the knowledge of the person concerned but should also make it possible for the workers to attain a certain level of independence, and services offered should be competitive with other firms. Part of the operating costs of the disabled person's workshop should be recouped by the proceeds of the work done.

Employees receive adequate (legally agreed) remuneration. According to the principles of solidarity all employees of the workshop are equally paid from one pot. MOL also pays a 'performance improvement' wage. This takes into account the punctuality and tidiness of the employees, among other factors.

The Diakonie-Werkstätten Berlin gGmbH is operated by two church bodies. There are three workshops, employing 660 people supervised by 150 staff. The main aim is the social and vocational integration of mentally handicapped persons. Activities carried out include assembly operations, gardening, housekeeping, laundry work, and paper processing.

The Diakonie-Werkstatt Weißensee started offering the building cleaning service in 2001, and it was placed on a commercial footing in 2004. MOL has been offering a cleaning service since 1991. The introduction of a cleaning service was made easier because a specialist cleaning company provided technical support, and offered cleaning supplies at a competitive rate.

4.4.2. Aims and Objectives

The most important purpose of the disabled person's workshops is to break down the differences between handicapped people and others. Individuals with disabilities are enabled to carry out appropriate activities that they can perform largely independently. It is also important to offer a service that is commercially competitive.

4.4.3. Scope of the project — what was done

Cleaning was selected because it offers possibilities for the employees to develop professionally, and to earn an income.

The selection of employees for cleaning tasks is done by the workshop within the scope of the general vocational training programme. In the first year all employees learn about all the work areas, including cleaning. In the second year one of four training periods is completed in the cleaning area. After this, employees decide which area they want to specialise in, depending on their aptitudes and the judgement of the supervisors. For cleaning, one special focus of the further vocational training is the development of fine-motor abilities.

The practical daily work routine must be adapted to the special requirements of these workers.

- Reduce risks in the work area as much as possible; simplify working procedures and the use of equipment and cleaning agents.
- Regulate and structure the work routine so that employees feel secure and confident in carrying out their tasks.
- Provide continuous education and training for the employees.

The employees must be able to handle equipment properly and safely. Few are allowed to work with electrical equipment. As far as cleaning agents are concerned, only a small range of products are used, to avoid confusion. Three to four products are usually sufficient for the normal range of cleaning activities. The wearing of personal protective equipment is strictly enforced: gloves and protective glasses are routinely carried.

Work processes are adapted to the abilities of the employees. All employees work in teams of three or four people. A workshop staff member accompanies and is responsible for two teams at a time.

Unlike conventional cleaning, each employee is not responsible for cleaning a whole room. Each room is cleaned by the team, and each team member has a specific task. For example, one person empties the wastepaper baskets while another cleans the mirrors. The group leader starts every day with a work meeting. The tasks are discussed with each employee, and then the cleaning trolleys are prepared. Cleaning fluids are supplied in dosing bottles and provided diluted in cleaning buckets. If they have to be used undiluted, the cleaning will be done either by the staff member or under his constant supervision.

The staff members are responsible for supervising the working routines, ensuring that the customers are satisfied. If an employee makes good progress in his job, he can take on more responsibility — perhaps by organising the work routines alone.

These cleaning services are not extensively advertised, but usually hired by word of mouth or through the Internet. MOL also distributes flyers and participates in information open days, as well as applying for cleaning tenders.

4.4.4. Results and evaluation of the project

In both cases, the goals of the workshops are achieved. By offering a competitive cleaning service the employees are successfully integrated into the job market. However, a lasting integration can only be attained in good economic circumstances. Due to the downturn in the German labour market, especially in eastern Germany, no employee has yet been able to get a job at a professional cleaning company.

4.4.5. Problems faced

In developing such a service field with mentally handicapped people it is important to have a staff member with professional cleaning work experience. Developing work routines for such employees is likely to require expert assistance in drawing up cleaning plans, training and advising on the handling of chemicals and work equipment.

The use of ladders is problematic for the Diakonie-Werkstätten. For safety reasons the employees may never use a ladder unattended, which makes such jobs uneconomic as too many supervisors are required.

The number of possible clients is limited, because the workshops only carry out daytime cleaning. It is also important that the cleaning activity includes a routine, so one-off or sporadic assignments cannot be undertaken.

4.4.6. Success factors

The workshops offer demanding work with development possibilities for mentally disabled persons. Cleaning work can be differentiated according to a person's abilities and development. It provides an opportunity to enter the job market. The employees are properly paid; they operate in public areas and are perceived and treated like 'ordinary' workers.

Clients who use such cleaning services are seen to be demonstrating social responsibility. In addition, commercial clients get a tax rebate if they use such services[94]. This means the services of mentally disabled persons are cost-neutral and can be offered at market prices.

4.4.7. Transferability of the project

The working procedures could be adopted in their entirety, but similar projects would have to take account of regulations concerning the employment of workers with disabilities in various Member States. Projects such as these seem to be more difficult to accomplish if the general price level for cleaning services in a Member State is low or if the market is particularly competitive.

In terms of transferability, it is important to consider who will pay the wages of the staff members and the costs of the workshop buildings. In Germany these costs are assumed by responsible bodies (ecclesiastical foundation, life assistance body), which are almost entirely financed by the state. The income gained from the cleaning activity is available for wages, performance improvement bonuses and the purchase of machinery and equipment. Hence, an important factor in transferability is the availability of state subsidies, whether direct or indirect.

94 Paragraph 77 SGB IX, Ausgleichsabgabe, 'Neuntes Buch Sozialgesetzbuch — Rehabilitation und Teilhabe behinderter Menschen — (Artikel 1 des Gesetzes vom 19. Juni 2001, BGBl. I S. 1046), zuletzt geändert durch Artikel 28 Abs. 1 des Gesetzes vom 7. September 2007 (BGBl. I S. 2246)' (http://bundesrecht.juris.de/sgb_9/__77.html).

4.4.8. Details of initiative

Table 44: Enabling people with disabilities to work as cleaners

Title	Enabling people with disabilities to work as cleaners
Type of project	Creation and extension of a work division, lasting occupation of mentally handicapped persons
Focus	Social services, building cleaners
Lead organisation	(a) Diakonie-Werkstätten Berlin gGmbH, Werkstatt Weißensee (Diakonie workshops of Berlin gGmbH, workshop Weissensee) (b) Märkisch-Oderland Werkstätten Lebenshilfe e.V. — MOL (Märkisch-Oderland workshops life assistance e.V. — MOL)
Contact	(a) Diakonie-Werkstätten Berlin GmbH Mrs Petra Wosnik, workshop leader Werkstatt Weißensee, Nachtalbenweg 50, 13088 Berlin, GERMANY Tel. +49 3096276620, Fax +49 3096276619 E-mail: wsee@stephanus-verbund.de http://www.diakoniewerkstatt.com (b) Märkisch-Oderland Werkstätten Lebenshilfe MOL e.V. Mrs Angelika Langisch, workshop leader Am Biotop 24, 15344 Strausberg, GERMANY Tel. +49 3341305402, Fax +49 3341305647 E-mail: wfb@lebenshilfe-mol.de http://www.lebenshilfe-mol.de
Other partners	Specialised company for professional cleaning technology
Date of project	(a) started in 2001, permanently since 2004; (b) since 1991, ongoing

4.5. Customised safety and health training for cleaners (Greece)

- Customised occupational safety and health training courses for cleaning services

4.5.1. Introduction

OIKOMET SA is a cleaning services company established in 2001 with about 800 employees, based in Piraeus. The company has contracts with the Urban Railway (HSAP) and the Hellenic Railways Organisation (OSE). HSAP has specified in its cleaning services' procurement regulations that occupational safety and health training will be provided for a number of workers by its Safety Engineers. Additionally OIKOMET SA has initiated further training courses in collaboration with the Hellenic Institute for Occupational Health & Safety (ELINYAE).

4.5.2. Aims and objectives

The aim of the programme was to equip trainees with knowledge and expertise in the area of health and safety. The programme was aimed at workers with the

minimum mandatory education level, and migrant workers. It is hoped that the knowledge acquired by workers, and the diffusion of information, will enable them to carry out their jobs more safely.

ECOMET SA (Ecological — Mechanical — Commercial — Technical — Security — Real Estate — SA) took the initiative to organise a training seminar on occupational safety and health. The company wanted to express in this way its awareness of occupational risks prevention. However, the procurement of the urban railway contract for cleaning services that included occupational safety and health training was a momentum to this action.

4.5.3. Scope of the project — what was done

In December 2006, two seminars lasting a total of 24 hours each were organised, with 39 attendees in all. The seminar trainers were staff from the Hellenic Institute of Occupational Health & Safety (ELINYAE). They all had a postgraduate qualification and at least five years of professional experience. The cost of the two seminars was EUR 5 700. Funding was ensured through a special Account for Employment and Vocational Training (LAEK) to which all employers contribute.

Table 45: Seminar programme

Day	Topics	Duration (hours)
1	Health and safety at work	1
	Work environment	2
2	Physical agents	1
	Occupational safety and health signing — PPE (first part)	1
	Work equipment — principles of safety	1
3	Carcinogens	1
	Electrical safety	2
4	Chemical agents at the workplace	1
	Biological agents at the workplace	2
5	Occupational safety and health signing (second part)	2
	Thermal environment	1
6	PPE (second part)	2
	Portable work equipment	1
7	Ergonomics — MSDs	3
8	First aid	3

4.5.4. Evaluation and transferability of the project

The result of the training programme was to increase workers' awareness of safety and health matters. Trainees were impressed by the high level of the programme. Out of the 800 people that the company employs only 50 were selected to attend the programme (only 40 attended, due to night shifts and limited free time). One success factor was that

ELINYAE had developed a tailor-made programme for the company and its workplaces taking into account its specific characteristics. The fact that the safety and health training was mandatory for the subcontractors gave considerable momentum to the initiative. The training approach and the programme itself can be easily transferred as the themes covered are common in all areas of the cleaning sector.

4.5.5. Details of initiative

Table 46: OSH training for cleaners

Title	Occupational safety and health training for cleaners
Type of project	Occupational safety and health training
Lead organisation	ELINYAE
Other organisation(s)	OIKOMET SA
Date of project	12/2006
Contact details	Dimitra Veneti, Training Centre, Hellenic Institute for Occupational Health & Safety (ELINYAE) 143 Liosion & Theirsiou 6, Athens, 10445, GREECE Tel. +30 2108200136, Fax +30 2108200222 E-mail: veneti@elinyae.gr Christos Chatziioannou, Head of Training Centre, Hellenic Institute for Occupational Health & Safety (ELINYAE) E-mail: chatziioannou@elinyae.gr

4.6. Training cleaning workers to prevent chemical spills (Spain)

- A training and educational programme for workers' representatives in the cleaning sector in Spain
- Educating cleaners in the prevention of risks caused by chemical substances in their work environment

4.6.1. Introduction

There are 8 500 companies in the cleaning sector in Spain, and 80 % of them deal with the inside of buildings. They employ 246 000 workers, 70 % of whom are women. Cleaners have to work in a wide range of environments: office buildings, health centres, factories, abattoirs, shopping centres, private homes, etc. The areas to be cleaned include offices, bathrooms, kitchens, gardens, corridors, stores, factory premises, operating theatres and many more. The surfaces can vary from metal, glass or plastic, to tiles, wood, fabrics, etc. If we add to this variety of workplaces, spaces

and surfaces the different types of dirt and materials they have to deal with (soil, dust, grease, paint, food, sharp objects, etc.), then it is easy to understand why there are thousands of different cleaning products in the market, containing hundreds of ingredients representing different levels of hazards.

Some of these products include harmful substances, and almost all are either irritating or corrosive. Many also contain substances that can cause skin problems and allergies. Possible adverse health effects include burns; irritation of the ear, nose and throat; damage to the central nervous system, kidneys, liver, lungs, and the reproductive system. Infections and needlestick injuries are also common in some settings. Additionally, some products cause serious damage to the environment (e.g. sodium hypochlorite, alkyl phenols, etc.).

However, little attention has been paid to the health and safety of cleaners handling these dangerous substances. The situation is complicated further where cleaning services are subcontracted, so that the cleaners are not directly employed by the organisation(s) at whose premises they are working.

The actual case study was reported by Instituto Sindical de Trabajo, Ambiente y Salud (ISTAS), a self-managed trade union technical foundation supported by the Spanish Trade Union Confederation (CC.OO) to promote the improvement of working conditions, occupational health and safety and environmental protection in Spain.

4.6.2. Aims and objectives

Given the lack of training in risk prevention, it was decided to implement a specific training and educational programme for workers' representatives in the cleaning sector. This initiative had two primary goals: to facilitate cleaners' involvement in the prevention of risks caused by chemical substances at work and to help them apply the practical knowledge acquired during the training to improve health and safety conditions at their workplace. This was done by raising awareness and providing information about risks involved in the handling of chemical substances.

4.6.3. Scope of the project — what was done

The training programme was developed in collaboration with the Regional Secretariat of Environment and Occupational Health of Comisiones Obreras in the region of Aragón, and was specifically designed for workers' 'prevention delegates'. Over 1 000 delegates took part in the training covering cleaning staff in banks, hospitals, factories, local government buildings and private dwellings. The companies were selected with the aim of obtaining a wide dissemination of the information, from participants to delegates in other companies, thus reaching a large number of workers. Women were specifically targeted for the training programme. The delegates were employed by the companies mentioned in the table below.

Table 47: Companies involved

Company	Activity	No of workers
Tiebel Sociedad Cooperativa	Cleaning of offices, factory premises, private homes, etc.	30
Limpiezas Laurbe	Cleaning of Ibercaja bank offices	250
Valymsa S.A.	Cleaning of Hospital Clínico Universitario	192
CCP	Cleaning of buildings and public centres belonging to Zaragoza's town hall	300
Maconsi	Cleaning of Hospital Miguel Servet	300

The difficult working conditions in the sector affected the participants in several ways: many suffered changes of employer and subcontracts throughout the course and had to drop out, or found it impossible to participate because of their workload. With only one exception, delegates received basic risk prevention training provided by the trade union, as well as a 20-hour course provided by their company. However, they had little knowledge about: risk assessment or how to interpret information about chemical risks; tools to identify the chemical substances present in their workplace; good practices to reduce risk; or criteria to select less dangerous products. The training course covered:

- obtaining and analysing information from labels or safety datasheets;
- risk prevention tools, including making proposals for substituting high-risk products with lower risk products;
- information about cleaning processes and how products work;
- presenting proposals to employers.

The training programme aimed to help the participants learn from their own experience, while trainers acted as facilitators. The work was carried out in groups, at times and dates agreed by all in order to facilitate attendance. Six group sessions were held combined with one assessment or personalised tutorial session. The sessions were organised in a logical sequence, starting from general subjects such as regulations and risk prevention, to more specific issues such as information about chemical products and risks, disinfection processes, selecting disinfecting products, etc.

A crucial aspect of the training process is the transfer of knowledge from the learning environment to the workplace. The aim was that theoretical knowledge would be applied immediately at the company throughout the course. Each delegate carried out initiatives at their own company. Starting from a brief presentation made by the trainer, the delegates used their company's data and experience to assess the risks that the cleaning products they used could pose for health and the environment. Group work allowed delegates to learn about practices and experiences in other companies. Using this information, they considered the different strategies for intervention and planned the best alternative for their particular case. In the following session the results were analysed by the group.

4.6.4. Results and evaluation of the project

The programme has resulted in various benefits. The financial cost of the training activity was not high, while the benefits in terms of awareness-raising and short and long-term prevention are good. A large number of immediate interventions were generated after the programme. These included the substitution, elimination

or control of dangerous substances, which resulted in immediate health and environmental improvements. Delegates developed a better perception of their job and its status, and greater confidence to speak with, negotiate and present proposals to their employers.

Following the course, the participants were able to apply their knowledge to the workplace in a variety of ways, including discussing issues with employers and informing other workers of risks and the proposals to prevent them. They learned how to ask the company for information about risks caused by dangerous substances, and how to obtain the labels and safety datasheets of the products and analyse them. Delegates in two thirds of the companies presented a proposal to the management for the substitution of dangerous products with lower-risk alternatives.

4.6.5. Challenges and successes

As explained above, many participants changed company or subcontract during the course and were forced to drop out, or found it impossible to participate because of their workload.

However, this case covers a sector that is not usually a focus of attention, despite employing a high number of workers. The participatory approach described here, with its emphasis on the practical application of knowledge, may help in a sector where it is often difficult to ensure that the necessary information reaches the mobile workers.

4.6.6. Transferability of the project

With support from the Asociación de Mutuas de Accidentes de Trabajo y Enfermedades Profesionales de la Seguridad Social — AMAT (the association of social security work accident and occupational disease insurance organisations), ISTAS edited the information and experience collected in this programme into a guide for prevention delegates entitled *Guide for the elimination of toxic substances in the cleaning sector*. It also organised a conference aimed at prevention delegates in the cleaning sector from all over Spain.

4.6.7. Details of initiative

Table 48: Training cleaning workers to prevent chemical risks

Title	Training cleaning workers to prevent chemical risks
Type of project	A training and educational programme for workers' representatives in the cleaning sector in Spain
Lead organisation	Instituto Sindical de Trabajo, Ambiente y Salud (ISTAS)
Other organisation(s) involved	Regional Secretariat of Environment and Occupational Health of Comisiones Obreras (Aragón)
Date of project	2001–02
Contact details	Dolores Romano Instituto Sindical de Trabajo, Ambiente y Salud (ISTAS) DROMANO@ISTAS.NET C/ General Cabrera 21, 28020 Madrid, SPAIN E-mail: istas@istas.ccoo.es

4.7. Designing hotel rooms with cleaning in mind (France)

- Renovation of hotel rooms to improve the working conditions of the room cleaners
- Full-scale testing by both staff and customers of three model rooms

4.7.1. Introduction

The four-star luxury Scribe Hotel is a venerable institution. Located in a 19th century building in the ninth arrondissement of Paris, it has no fewer than 40 types of rooms, two of which are attic rooms. It is being completely renovated, and in an effort to improve the working conditions of the room-cleaning staff the architect in charge of the project has designed model rooms which the workers have been able to test. This produced a wealth of information that could be used productively when drawing up the final design.

As part of a total refurbishment project the hotel hired the services of an architect, chosen not only for his talent but also his flexibility. 'We did not hire someone from the hotel industry, but someone who would be capable of something flexible and functional for an establishment that is required to manage more than 200 rooms each day', explained Managing Director Philippe Azière. 'We had to find a compromise enabling us to retain the authenticity of the style and the design while translating it into a hotel establishment approach.'

4.7.2. Aims and scope of the project

The objective of the Scribe Hotel in creating model rooms was to get critical feedback from the chambermaids and ensure that the future rooms of the Scribe would be designed to prevent occupational risks insofar as possible. Three model rooms were identified as being broadly representative of the situations found in the establishment.

Management outlined the project to the chambermaids, emphasising the attention paid to their problems while asking them to try out the rooms to ensure they met their needs. Following the tests, analysis of the critical comments made it possible to distinguish between undeniable problems and mere resistance to change in the workplace. Involving the chambermaids in the project, and preparing them for the changes, was invaluable in helping gain acceptance for the changed working conditions.

The characteristics of the new Scribe rooms are as follows:

- Room — wall-mounted television set, small-sized furniture (console, armchair, etc.) to save space, correspondence folder to prevent stationery from becoming scattered, light waste bin (the previous one was made of Corian, a heavy material), flush wall sockets, choice of fabrics that do not show the dirt (no more velour armchairs!), elimination of curtain cords, reduction in the number of skirting boards which are, moreover, placed higher up.

- Bathroom — choice of smooth ceramics that do not show the dirt for the ceramics, suspended WCs for ease of cleaning, plastic coverings for dressing gowns, etc.
- Tools — provision of feather dusters, research on trolley manoeuvrability, etc.

4.7.3. Results and transferability of the project

The experience has proved to be positive as the design of the rooms has been carefully adapted to the needs of the cleaners. It is always difficult to change working practices and this can be a cause of stress for workers, especially in a place like the Scribe Hotel where many cleaners have years of service. The management found it necessary to listen carefully to the workers and help them negotiate this phase successfully.

This action could be transferred easily to other hotels but it needs a strong commitment on the part of the management to consultation and achieving change.

4.7.4. Details of initiative

Table 49: Scribe Hotel — model rooms in the test phase

Title	Scribe Hotel — model rooms in the test phase
Type of project	Renovation of hotel rooms to improve the working conditions of the room cleaning staff
Focus	Hotel Sector
Lead organisation	Caisse Régionale d'Assurance Maladie d'Ile de France (CRAMIF)
Contact person	Christophe Ballue — CRAMIF
Other organisation(s)	Hotel Scribe
Date of project	2006–07
Further information	Travail et Sécurité No 09-06, pp. 24–26
Contact details	Christophe Ballue Caisse Régionale d'Assurance Maladie d'Ile-de-France Direction Régionale des risques Professionnels Antenne de Paris 17/19 avenue de Flandre, 75954 Paris Cedex 19, FRANCE Tel. +33 140053816, Fax +33 140053813 E-mail: christophe.ballue@cramif.cnamts.fr

Ergonomic analysis of three floor cleaning techniques (France)

Maintenance and cleaning of floors in healthcare environments are a priority and an integral part of efforts to prevent nosocomial infections [1]. The changes made in a Paris public hospital to improve the efficiency of floor cleaning and improve hygiene have also reduced the physical discomfort involved in the work. It was decided to evaluate the improvements brought about by the successive changes of cleaning techniques. This was carried out by the occupational

1 Nosocomial infections are infections resulting from treatment in a healthcare unit, but are secondary to the patient's original condition.

medicine department of the hospital, in cooperation with the manager of the biocleaning team.

Floor cleaning can be performed by techniques which differ according to the equipment used.

- Use of a swab soaked in a bucket of detergent for several rooms and then dried with a press placed on a second trolley. This technique is the only one that requires frequent changing of the bucket water, about every three rooms.
- Flat mop cleaning with a sponge pad used for a single room and dried using a press. Regular renewal of the bucket contents is no longer necessary, but the effort of drying the mop on the press is the same as with the swab.
- Flat mop cleaning with an impregnated sponge pad and then a disposable mop and a draining screen. This cleaning technique is the only one that eliminates press drying and requires a single trolley. It provides good results with a reduction in the physical workload.

The last-mentioned technique conformed to hospital hygiene rules. It eliminates the need for soaking in dirty water and repeated changing of the bucket water. A reduced amount of detergent is needed, and it does away with the need to carry heavy buckets.

Moreover, the new technique leaves the floor wet for only a short time, thus reducing the risks of falls and slips by other medical personnel, which are frequent causes of occupational injuries. With shorter waiting times, it is easier to ask medical personnel not to enter a wet room until the floor is dry. This ensures better hygienic and aesthetic results of cleaning and can facilitate relations between the biocleaning team and the medical care team [2].

2 Henry SC, Estryn-Behar M, Personne De Chaleix M, Guenane L, Fatmi S. 'Ergonomic analysis of floor cleaning by three techniques' DMT Ergonomie 74 TL 22.

4.8. Organisational and training plan — Greco Group (Italy)

- Reorganisation of responsibilities
- Improvement of supervision and training
- Decrease in occupational accidents

4.8.1. Introduction

The Greco Group is a cleaning contractor that employs approximately 2 500 workers throughout Italy. It operates in various environments such as hospitals, factories, supermarkets and shops, banks and offices. There is also a 'flying squad' which cleans building façades, fountains and monuments.

The cleaning sector has been going through a period of innovation and expansion both in the number of firms and the number of workers employed. The practice

of outsourcing is also increasing: in addition to traditional cleaning activities, these firms carry out other activities such as machinery and equipment maintenance or the maintenance of green spaces on behalf of companies and organisations that traditionally employed their own workers for these tasks.

Female workers are well represented in the cleaning sector and in central-southern Italy they are predominant, while a number of migrant workers have also entered the sector.

In Italy, most cleaning is now contracted out and companies have to be both mobile and flexible to gain often short-term contracts. There is high staff turnover and little professional recognition, and sometimes little attention is paid to health and safety at work.

Taking account of the variety of situations in which workers are required to operate, the risk profile of male and female cleaning firm workers has two different aspects: a set of risks may be drawn up based on the tasks carried out (cleaning offices and sanitary facilities, cleaning vehicles, maintenance of green areas and beaches) and another set of risks may be drawn up by reference to the specific risks associated with the environment where the cleaning activities are carried out.

For workers in health facilities, hotels, canteens and schools, an additional level of risk should be noted: biological risk. There are additional risks which should be taken into account in certain factories and manufacturing processes. On the other hand, workers operating in urban areas or in particular environments such as stations, ports or bus garages and vehicle depots are subject to risks associated with traffic pollution and the danger of being knocked down.

A further problem is that little health surveillance is carried out among cleaning service workers, partly because cleaning contractors are not legally obliged to employ an occupational physician.

4.8.2. Aims and Objectives

There was a recognition that some activities carried out on site are difficult to supervise and monitor, and that training needed to match the needs of both the cleaning workers and managers.

Two objectives were identified in particular to meet the overall goal of a reduction in the incidence of accidents at work — the improved supervision by operators in charge and a greater awareness on the part of workers of safety-related issues.

Promoting a culture of prevention in the company also meant promoting awareness of occupational safety issues amongst male and female workers, with the aim of helping them take a more active and conscious part in the company's decision-making process.

The decision to encourage workers' participation falls within a wider company strategy, namely to increase the status of a sector that has been placed at a disadvantage due to the perception of lower social standing, the existence of precarious working conditions and a widespread failure to comply with health and safety regulations.

4.8.3. Scope of the project — what was done

1. Plan to enhance the implementation of safety standards

A survey was conducted by the Greco Group to find out whether workers had implemented safety measures and it thus identified serious problems of an organisational nature within the company itself. A distinguishing feature of cleaning operations is that they are distributed over a wide territory. This means that it is difficult for the company to carry out frequent inspections to verify whether workers are carrying out their duties safely. The use of personal protective equipment and compliance with safety procedures is often considered to be a merely formal requirement by the workers; hence they may be operating in risky conditions where no inspections are performed. The critical issues identified here were the lack of a company safety culture, workers' behaviour, and the difficulty encountered by the company in carrying out inspections.

A plan was developed to enhance the implementation of safety standards by distributing responsibilities — including those for safety-related issues — among the key players in the company's organisation. According to the pattern of responsibilities, the technical team leader will be appointed as a Safety Prevention and Protection Services Operator (ASPP), thus ensuring the permanent presence in the workplace of a person who is responsible for verifying that workers carry out their duties in safety.

2. Company training plan for targeted training interventions

The implementation of a company training plan was deemed necessary to enhance the information flow relating to health and safety issues which, according to the company's policy, should involve all the departments within the company. Rather than implementing a formal training programme, it was decided to carry out a series of targeted initiatives focused specifically on the identified training needs.

The first level of information is based on the risks faced by individuals working in the cleaning service sector: for this reason, a booklet entitled *626 cleaning in safety* is given to workers when they are hired. This document is easily understandable by workers whose mother tongue is not Italian, as many explanatory illustrations are included. Another document focuses not only on the known risks, but also on the analysis of the workers' training needs. This booklet is the result of the cooperation between the Safety Prevention and Protection Services Managers (RSPP), the trainers and experts employed by the company. All workers also receive a basic initial level of training. For those job positions identified in the safety plan as being subject to specific risks, a second level of training is given.

The second level of training involves on-the-job training programmes specifically addressing the tasks and the relevant risks involved. The identified risks on which the specific training programme is based are:

- falling to the ground
- falling from a height
- electrocution
- chemical risk
- biological risk
- cutting accidents
- awkward postures and repetitive movements.

The job positions which are known to expose workers to risks and which, therefore, come within the framework of the training plan are those associated with hospital, industrial and chemical environments, warehouse management, as well as activities carried out by the flying squad and video display terminal operators.

In addition, there is a third level of training involving refresher courses which might be carried out in various circumstances: when someone changes job or there is a change in risk factors for a job, for example.

4.8.4. Results and evaluation of the project

Effects of the project included the following.

- Health and safety management was more effectively integrated into the company management system.
- By launching the organisational and training plan, the company management committed itself more strongly to the workers' health and safety.
- The involvement of various key players within the company hierarchy ensures continuity.
- All 2 500 of the company's workers were involved in some way.
- Cooperation improved between company management, safety prevention and protection services managers (RSPP) and workers' safety representatives (RLS). This kind of cooperation is especially vital when emergencies arise.
- According to the company, the intervention also resulted in a reduction in the number of accidents; however, no data were provided to confirm this.

4.8.5. Problems faced

The problems which emerged before and during the management of the project included the lack of a company safety culture, inappropriate worker behaviour, and the difficulty faced by management in carrying out supervision.

The project was based on the belief that a higher level of worker awareness and participation in company decision-making are key factors in improving occupational health and safety, but whether such a policy will turn out to be successful is a matter of time. In other words, the action may not give immediate results but must be subject to evaluation on a long-term basis.

A further aspect which should not be neglected relates to the outsourcing of services by way of tenders, which often results in a change of the contracting company without involving a change of personnel. This means that the workers in question remain in their jobs while the company employing them changes. Because of this, the same workers may over a period of time be employed by a company which values the safety of its workers, only to find afterwards that — without changing their jobs — they are employed by a company that merely pays lip-service to safety issues.

All of this can impinge upon the effectiveness of the project, through no fault of the company which respects these values. The causes in question extend well beyond the control of the company itself, but it must take account of them if it is to comply with its legal responsibilities and organise itself effectively.

4.8.6. Success factors

The success factors of the action included;

- assigning control and supervision tasks to the production managers permitted the continuous monitoring of the behaviour of the workers, and allowed identification of areas where they showed poor training; monitoring has also allowed the inclusion of existing risks in the training, not just the risks initially anticipated;
- in relation to the training process, on the other hand, the decision to take two routes, that of general training and that of on-the-job training, allowed the company to modify and update the training courses to make them more relevant to the actual training needs of the workers.

4.8.7. Transferability of the project

The problems confronted by the Greco Group are fairly typical of the sector, i.e. contracting out company activities (outsourcing), mobility of companies and of workers, fragmentation of areas of intervention, limited expertise and professionalism of workers, and the approaches taken by the enterprise can be applied in other businesses.

Any ad hoc plan suitable for application to other working contexts in the sector, should take account of the following factors in particular:

- the technical team leader should not be perceived merely as a figure who is required to carry out exclusively supervisory tasks; rather he/she should be seen as a professional whose authority is based on his/her competence, his/her support and the due recognition of his/her role by company management;
- in the training activities addressed to workers, it is crucial to take into account cultural issues as these can impact on risk perception;
- it is also necessary to take account of the linguistic difficulties of migrant workers.

4.8.8. Details of initiative

Table 50: Organisational and training plans

Title	Organisational and training plan
Type of project	Intervention measures to integrate the management of safety into the company organisation and coherent training plans
Focus	Work organisation and training
Lead organisation	Greco Group
Date of project	January 2006
Contact information	Mr Aldo Greco, Managing Director Greco Group Via Imperia 18, 20142 Milan, ITALY Tel. +39 023041921, Fax +39 0289549833 E-mail: gruppogreco@gruppogreco.com

Mapping of risks from repetitive upper limb movements in chambermaids (Italy) 4.9.

- Chambermaids are at high risk of MSDs because of their specific working activity
- The risks from upper limb overload due to repetitive work can be reduced by proper risk assessment and educational programmes

4.9.1. Introduction

Chambermaids represent a high-risk group with regard to musculoskeletal disorders because of their specific working activity. For this reason, an Italian hotel asked CEMOC (Occupational Medicine Centre) and Studio FANTI to conduct a study on risks from upper limb overload in hotel room cleaners. A medical specialist and an engineer carried out an inspection at the hotel in July 2002 during which they took video films, interviewed workers and held meetings with company experts. The hotel's housekeeper took part in the inspection and provided all information needed to carry out the risk assessment relating to the tasks ordinary cleaning of a room and heavy cleaning of a room.

Table 51: Cleaning process — ordinary room

No	Description	% [95]
1	Opening windows and curtains	2
2	Stripping bedroom and bathroom	10
3	Controlling minibar	3
4	Using vacuum cleaner or carpet sweeper	13
5	Cleaning bathroom	17
6	Restocking bathroom	17
7	Making up the beds	17
8	Dusting the bedroom	17
9	Restocking the minibar	3
10	Pulling and pushing trolley	2

95 % = percentage duration of total process.

Table 52: Cleaning process — heavy cleaning

No	Description	%[96]
1	Stripping bedroom	8
2	Using vacuum cleaner and/or feather duster for ceilings	6
3	Washing furniture	33
4	Cleaning bathroom with steam cleaner	15
5	Cleaning and drying of bathroom	35
6	Replacement of bedlinen and mattress covers	3

The percentages refer to an average situation which represents activities carried out by each worker over the course of one year. It should be noted that the ordinary cleaning of rooms is done on a daily basis by specific personnel. Heavy cleaning activities, on the other hand, are carried out for about two weeks per year by each employee assigned to the task.

4.9.2. Aims and objectives

The project aimed to identify risks from upper limb overload due to repetitive work affecting hotel room cleaners. The following core risk factors were identified and quantified which, taken together, characterise occupational exposure in proportion to their respective duration:

- inadequate recovery time
- high frequency of actions
- application of excessive force
- awkward or forced postures and movements of the upper limbs.

4.9.3. Scope of the project — what was done

The following general stages were carried out:

- identification of the typical tasks of a particular job and, of these, those tasks performed (often or for a long time) in repeated and identical cycles;
- identification of the sequence of technical actions involved in the work cycles of each specific task ;
- description and quantification of the risk factors for each representative work cycle: frequency, force, posture, additional factors;
- reorganisation of the data relating to the cycles in accordance with the tasks and the entire work shift, taking into account the durations and sequences of the various tasks and periods of recovery;
- concise and integrated assessment of the risk factors relating to the working activity as a whole.

In analysing occupational tasks, the OCRA checklist was used, which is a method suited to compiling the map of risk for exposure to occupational activities involving repetitive movements of the upper limbs.

96 % = percentage duration of total process.

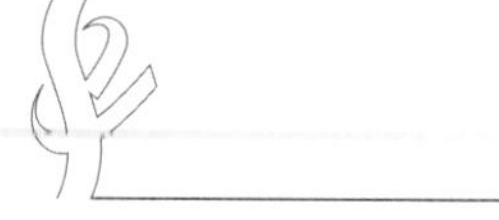

The OCRA checklist includes the analysis of all the principal risk factors such as:

- lack of recovery time
- frequency
- force
- awkward posture
- additional risk factors.

Table 53: Checklist for cleaning standard room — ordinary cleaning

No	Description of the work phases	Recov.	freq·	force	side	shoulder	Wrist	elbow	hand	stereotypy	total posture	Add	Checklist Value
1	Opening windows and curtains	0.5	0	0	/	0	0	0	0	0	0	0	**0.5**
2	Stripping bedroom and bathroom	0.5	4	0	Both	3	3	3	5	0	5	0	**9.5**
3	Controlling minibar	0.5	0	0	/	0	0	0	0	0	0	0	**0.5**
4	Using vacuum cleaner or carpet sweeper	0.5	5.5	0	Right	4	2	4	0	0	4	0	**10.0**
5	Cleaning bathroom	0.5	7	0	Right	4	4	4	4.5	0	4.5	0	**12.0**
6	Restocking the bathroom	0.5	1	0	Right	1	1	0	4	0	4	0	**5.5**
7	Making up the bed	0.5	3	0	Both	4	4	4	4	0	4	0	**7.5**
8	Dusting the bedroom	0.5	7	0	Right	4	4	4	6	0	6	0	**13.5**
9	Restocking the minibar	0.5	w0	0	/	0	0	0	0	0	0	0	**0.5**
10	Pulling and pushing trolley	0.5	0	1	/	0	0	0	0	0	0	0	**1.5**
	Mean	**0.5**	**4.1**	**0.0**		**3.0**	**2.7**	**2.8**	**3.6**	**0.0**	**4.1**	**0.0**	**8.8**

Table 54: Checklist for cleaning standard room — heavy cleaning

No	Description of the work phases	Recov.	freq	force	side	shoulder	Wrist	elbow	hand	stereotypy	total posture	Add	Checklist Value
1	Stripping bedroom	0.5	5	0	Both	3	3	3	5	0	5	0	**10.5**
2	Use of vacuum cleaner and/ or feather duster for ceilings	0.5	3.5	0	Both	7	6	2	0	1	8	0	**12.0**
3	Washing furniture	0.5	7	0	Right	4	4	4	4.5	2	6.5	0	**14.0**
4	Cleaning bathroom with steam iron cleaners	0.5	3.5	0	Both	4	3	4	0	2	6	0	**10.0**
5	Cleaning and drying of bathroom	0.5	7	0	Right	4	4	4	4.5	2	6.5	0	**14.0**
6	Replacement of bedlinings and mattress covers	0.5	4	1	Both	3	3	1	5	0	5	0	**10.5**
	Mean	**0.5**	**6.0**	**0.0**		**4.1**	**3.9**	**3.7**	**3.6**	**1.7**	**6.3**	**0.0**	12.9

With the checklists, the information allows the risk level to be assessed following this scheme; see Table 55.

Table 55: Assessment scheme for risk identification

Level	Colour	Checklist	OCRA
Risk absent	Green	Up to 6	2
Low risk	Yellow	6.1–11.9	2.1–3.9
Medium risk	Red	12–18.9	4–7.9
High	Lilac	19 and beyond	8 and beyond

Methods of risk analysis in work cycles of long duration

In this particular occupational context, activities were broken down into separate phases of around 10 minutes or longer. Workers were filmed carrying out these activities, and the film footage was studied in slow motion to determine the risk value for that phase. Work phases were then categorised into four groups, ranging from high to no risk.

4.9.4. Results and evaluation of the project

The tables below show what percentages of work tasks fell into each category, firstly for standard cleaning and then for a 'heavy clean' of a room.

Table 56: Standard room — ordinary cleaning

	Total No work phase	%	No men	No women	%
HIGH Risk	0	0	0	0	0
MEDIUM Risk	0.33	33	0	0.33	33
LOW Risk	0.40	40	0	0.40	40
Risk ABSENT	0.27	27	0	0.27	27
Total	1		0	1	

Table 57: Heavy cleaning

	Total No work phase	%	No men	No women	%
HIGH Risk	0	0.0	0	0	0.0
MEDIUM Risk	0.74	73.9	0	0.74	73.9
LOW Risk	0.26	26.1	0	0.26	26.1
Risk ABSENT	0	0.0	0	0	0.0
Total	1		0	1	

For ordinary room cleaning, 33 % of the phases fall within the red band, 40 % in the yellow band, and 27 % in the green band, while for heavy cleaning, 74 % of the phases fall within the red band and 26 % fall in the yellow band.

In relation to chambermaids' activity, the phases demonstrating highest risk (red band) were bathroom cleaning and dusting; in relation to heavy cleaning in particular, attention should be drawn to the use of vacuum cleaners to clean the ceilings: this involves the overload of the shoulder joints, even when the relevant durations are short.

Generally, work carried out by the chambermaids involves a moderate overload of the wrist joints (high frequency of wrist movements in the use of cloth or sponge), of the elbow and of the shoulder (significant flexion-extension movements where larger surfaces are cleaned), and especially on the right side. Brief pauses in activity are important in containing risk.

Care should be taken in the use of sprays to clean bathrooms: operation of the spray button increases the number of the actions performed by the right hand, thus resulting in overloading of the joints of the first few fingers.

Regarding the movement of the trolley to restock the rooms: although this is not a repetitive activity, it should be noted that moving the trolley involves a loading of horizontal force equal to 13–14 kg (peak value) and 6–8 kg (maintenance value).

Using wheeled models which are better adapted to transferring loads across carpets — larger wheels that swivel — helps reduce the thrust load and makes the trolley more manageable; the push posture adopted by the worker can be improved by optimising the push-bar, with beneficial effects to the back as well as the wrists.

It may be noted — even if this does not relate to the biomechanical analysis of the upper limbs — that the posture assumed by chambermaids when carrying out their tasks often includes the bending of the back (approximately 25 % of the time); even where weights are not being lifted, this involves a functional overload of the structures of the lumbar-sacral rachis (disks, ligaments and muscles) which produces frequent episodes of lumbago.

4.9.5. Problems faced

When carrying out risk analysis on work cycles of long duration (more than about 10 minutes), it was found impossible to analyse and enumerate all the individual actions. In such cases, 'subgroups' were identified — shorter phases that characterised the task in question.

4.9.6. Success factors

Obtaining exhaustive mapping of the risks from repetitive upper limbs movements in work carried out by room cleaners allowed the hotel management to carry out a thorough risk assessment and prevent work-related ailments among its cleaners. The added value was the participation of the hotel's housekeeper in the initial inspection for the provision of all information needed to carry out the risk assessment.

4.9.7. Transferability of the project

The procedures for the mapping of the risks from repetitive upper limb movements through the 'OCRA checklist' is a user-friendly method that could be applied in other working environments and countries.

4.9.8. Details of initiative

Table 58: Mapping of risks from repetitive upper limb movements in working activities performed by hotel cleaners

Title	Mapping of risks from repetitive upper limb movements in working activities performed by hotel room cleaners
Type of project	Study on the identification of the risks from upper limb overload due to repetitive work affecting hotel room cleaners Mapping of the risks to support the risk assessment
Focus	Hotel cleaning activities
Lead organisations	Centro Medicina Occupazionale CEMOC (Occupational Medicine Centre — CEMOC) Studio FANTI
Date of project	2002
Contact information	CEMOC — Centro Medicina Occupazionale, IPC Milano Via R. Villasanta 11, 20145 Milan, ITALY Daniela Colombini E-mail: daniela.colombini@fastwebnet.it Studio FANTI -Analisi MTM/UAS, OCRA, NIOSH Michele Fanti E-mail: studiofantiergo@virgilio.it

4.10. Daytime cleaning at the Ministry of Social Affairs and Employment (Netherlands)

- Shift from night to day cleaning

4.10.1. Introduction

In 2003 a covenant on health and safety for the cleaning and window cleaning industry was signed[97]. A health and safety covenant, or arboconvenant, is an agreement outlining the working conditions in a given industry, which is concluded between the authorities (the Ministry of Social Affairs and Employment), employers and employee organisations. In the case of the covenant for the cleaning industry the organisations included the employer's organisation, Schoonmaak- en Bedrijfsdiensten (OSB), and the trade unions FNV Bondgenoten and CNV BedrijvenBond. Together the different parties wanted to improve working conditions and try to reduce risks, absenteeism and occupational accidents by means of this covenant. The covenant ran from 9 April 2003 to 1 March 2006.

One of the organisational measures laid down in the covenant's action plan was the promotion of daytime cleaning[98]. As a covenant party, the Ministry of Social

97 Available online (http://docs.minszw.nl/pdf//111/2003/111_2003_4_35872.pdf).

98 Plan van Aanpak Arboconvenant Schoonmaak- en Glazenwassersbranche, 9 April 2003, p. 17. Available online (http://docs.minszw.nl/pdf//113/2004/113_2004_4_39254.pdf).

Affairs and Employment committed itself to promote daytime cleaning among all government bodies and government-subsidised institutions. A pilot project was launched in 2003 in one of the office buildings of the ministry in The Hague.

The cleaning profession is neither glamorous nor easy. Cleaning is a physically taxing job with a low public perception. The turnover in the cleaning industry is considerable, and the level of absenteeism is high.

Cleaning outside of normal working hours can make the job harder for many workers[99].

- Cleaners do not always see their job as a real job but more as something of a 'gap-filler', as they work outside the normal hours when no one else is around.
- Cleaners have to work and go home at 'unsociable' hours, which might raise some security problems (it can be more dangerous at night), transport problems and difficulties combining work with family life.
- The job becomes unfeasible for people with vision issues after dark.
- There is a lack of contact and communication between the different parties involved (the client, building occupants, cleaning staff and operational manager). This can be detrimental for the cleaners because there is nobody around to direct questions to or to alert in the case of a technical problem, for example, and inconvenient for the building occupants as they are unable to notify cleaners of problems or show them their appreciation.
- There can be a decrease in efficiency and motivation among the cleaners because of working late and alone (workers may, for example, be tempted to take extra or extended breaks), so that more direct supervision is required.
- There is a higher energy bill as lights are kept on in the evenings/at night.
- There is often a duplication of services (e.g. a day porter or matron stocks restrooms during the day while a restroom specialist cleans the restrooms at night).

4.10.2. Aims and objectives

The aim of the pilot project was to switch from evening to daytime cleaning in an office building (with a gross surface area of 17 000 m^2) of the Ministry of Social Affairs and Employment (Beatrixpark, The Hague). This pilot was intended to demonstrate whether it was possible to organise daytime cleaning in an efficient manner and whether this approach was more beneficial than night-time cleaning. It was felt that a combination of daytime and evening cleaning would be necessary to ensure that the contract was properly executed. Certain work, such as floor mopping, is better done outside office hours. However, most cleaning tasks can easily be taken care of by day. Based on the pilot project the parties involved would then decide how daytime cleaning could be implemented throughout the entire ministry from 2005 onwards.

4.10.3. Scope of the project — what was done

In order to ensure the smoothest possible transition from daytime to evening cleaning, it was important to map out the most important factors likely to lead to success. The following factors were listed:

99 Based on Frank D. et al. 'Flipping the switch', Cleaning & Maintenance Management Magazine, 43(4), April 2006 available online (http://www.cmmonline.com/article.asp?IndexID=6636065) Virdi A. 'Seeing the light', European Cleaning Journal, available onine (http://www.europeancleaningjournal.com/index.php?option=com_content&task=view&id=219&Itemid=61).

- acceptance by the building's users, which depends to a large extent on the disturbance caused by the cleaning activities;
- the benefits and/or disadvantages experienced by cleaning staff themselves;
- the extent of further training of cleaning staff;
- the financial aspect: additional costs or potential cost savings.

A transition plan (project plan) could then be drawn up taking into account the above factors. In order to develop and implement such a plan, a project team was established. The team comprised ministry employees as well as employees of the cleaning contractor, HAGO Nederland BV, and a representative of the advice centre ATIR.

The project plan comprised the following 18 steps.

- Establish which activities qualified (or not) for daytime cleaning: 99 % of all work proved to be suited for daytime cleaning. The car park was excluded from this list for security reasons.
- Establish how many productive hours are needed in the evening and how many by day.
- Based on the above two steps, establish the most appropriate organisational structure.
- Analyse the difference between the existing (evening cleaning) and the new organisation (daytime cleaning).
- Draw up a transition schedule per division or space group (all parties involved opted in favour of a geographic transition).
- Develop a new division of tasks and job descriptions using an automated work management system.
- Implement the pilot's first phase:
    - inform users
    - implement effective transition
    - follow up pilot intensely during the first weeks
    - assessment (including conducting a user survey).
- Potential adjustment of the transition schedule based on the pilot.
- Presentation of the final transition plan to cleaning staff (employees had already been informed that the night-time activities were probably not of a permanent nature).
- Recruitment of new employees if necessary (if not enough employees were prepared to switch to daytime work).
- Conduct a campaign in each department to explain the benefits of the new situation to users and to promote acceptance: a brochure was left on each desk and information made available via the intranet.
- Re-instruct cleaning staff.
- Conduct a quality measurement to establish quality before the transition.
- Ensure the transition from evening cleaning to daytime cleaning per department.
- Conduct an in-depth quality measurement once a fortnight, over a period of six weeks, to point out and interpret any consequences for quality.
- Conduct an assessment, including a sample survey among users.
- If necessary, adapt working hours, the division of tasks and programmes based on the outcome of the assessment.
- Conclude project and dissolve project team.

4.10.4. Results and evaluation of the project

By 2005 daytime cleaning had been implemented throughout the entire building, in accordance with the project plan. The entire project was budget-neutral and there was no loss of quality involved. Due to the fact that cleaning staff were cleaning while users were working, it was possible to align cleaning activities with user requirements and to guarantee a faster reaction in case of problems. In addition daytime cleaning had a more preventive function: because the office workers saw the cleaners at work, they automatically had more respect for their work and were less inclined to leave behind a mess. Ninety percent of the workers in the building expressed their satisfaction with the transition.

Cleaning staff also expressed largely positive feelings with regard to the daytime cleaning project. After a period of time the cleaning company established that turnover and absenteeism rates had fallen. A fixed relation with the location and employees led to more satisfaction and employees taking more pleasure in their jobs. It also ensured that some employees learnt Dutch and Dutch behavioural standards. Employees are expected to speak Dutch and to have a more assertive attitude than they are used to. Thanks to daytime cleaning, workers can also work more hours and the combination with family life is facilitated. Sixty percent of all employees switched from evening to daytime cleaning. And, in line with the agreements made at the start of the project, other suitable work was found for those employees who did not wish to make the switch.

From November 2007 on, the Ministry of General Affairs will also make the transition to daytime cleaning, in cooperation with HAGO Nederland.

4.10.5. Problems faced

All parties were confronted with a number of issues during the project.

- Simultaneous working and cleaning results in a number of safety hazards, such as wet floors in coffee areas. This was solved by using warning signs in these locations.
- Some employees complained about noise disturbance due to vacuuming.
- Contact and communication between cleaning staff and users was difficult because not all employees had the same command of Dutch and many cleaners did not have the confidence to communicate with employees as 'equals'.
- Absenteeism even rose because tasks now took 3–5 hours a day instead of 2–2.5 hours for evening tasks.
- The reduced work capacity of several cleaners for medical reasons had a negative impact on the quality experienced by the building's users.

4.10.6. Success Factors

The following factors contributed to the project's success.

- Vacuuming took place during the early morning, when relatively few users are present.
- An inventory was made of the level of Dutch of the various cleaning staffers, and Dutch language courses were organised.
- A customised service training was developed, during which cleaning personnel were taught how to solve certain issues with users.

- The leadership style of the company manager is mainly aimed at the development of his/her cleaning personnel (behaviour and linguistic competence).
- There was an increase in employment and, in the long term, a reduction of absenteeism and staff turnover.
- The pilot took place in the ministry's main department.
- The pilot took place in a building that also housed the offices of the team that collaborated on the health and safety covenant for the cleaning and window cleaning industry, thus ensuring prior awareness and endorsement of the project.

4.10.7. Transferability of the project

The transition from night/evening to day cleaning can be made in different cleaning situations. Such a shift, however, requires certain practical adaptations and a real change in culture. Good planning and organisation are therefore needed. To determine whether a facility can be cleaned during the day, the following factors have to be considered [100]:

- the amount of foot traffic
- the type of machinery housed in the facility
- the equipment (desks, chairs, etc.) used by the occupants
- the events that take place in each building.

4.10.8. Contact information and details of initiative

Table 59: Daytime cleaning at the Ministry of Social Affairs and Employment

Title	Daytime cleaning at the Ministry of Social Affairs and Employment
Type of project	Pilot project for the transition from evening to daytime cleaning
Lead organisation	(a) Ministerie voor Sociale Zaken en Werk — SKW (Ministry of Social Affairs and Employment) (b) HAGO Nederland BV
Contact person	(a) Loek Helder, Teamleader Service Pand Beatrixpark, Anna van Hannoverstraat 4, 2595 BJ The Hague, NETHERLANDS Tel. +31 703336356 E-mail: lhelder@minszw.nl (b) Theo Bakker, operational manager Rivium 1e straat 75–79, Postbus 666, 2900 AR Capelle a/d IJssel, NETHERLANDS http://www.hago.nl
Date of project	Start in 2003

100 Based on: Frank D et al. 'Flipping the switch' (http://www.cmmonline.com/article.asp?IndexID=6636065).

MAS — Multicultural Amsterdam Cleaning company (Netherlands) 4.11.

- A cleaning company with a progressive policy regarding its employees
- Development of semi-skilled and unskilled immigrant cleaning staff.

4.11.1. Introduction

MAS Dienstverleners was founded in 1997 by Mrs Rahma el Mouden and her husband. Rahma el Mouden arrived in the Netherlands from Morocco at the age of 16. She started working as a cleaner and gradually worked her way up to supervisory level. At one point she was promised a promotion from assistant manager to manager. This promotion was refused because she was a woman and not proficient enough in Dutch. Rahma decided to leave her job and found her own company where an efficient and fair staff policy, aimed at the further development of mainly semi and unskilled immigrant cleaning staff, would be a priority.

Apart from providing traditional services like other cleaning companies, MAS pays particular attention to the well-being and the employability of its semi-skilled and unskilled immigrant cleaning staff. The company has an extensive and integrated staff policy with a focus on selection (initial) training, development, absenteeism and occupational health and safety. MAS's staff policy is based on respect for the employees and the company's motto is 'The customer is king, our employees are emperors'.

MAS now has over 200 customers for its cleaning, window cleaning and specialised cleaning services. The company has 300 employees, 280 of which are cleaners. Almost all employees are of immigrant origin; most have low education levels and are not fluent in Dutch. However, MAS offers them the chance to obtain a vocational certificate and attend language courses, improving their chances on the labour market.

4.11.2. Aims and scope of the project

MAS's integrated staff policy aims not only to benefit its clients by offering high-quality services, but to promote the well-being and employability of all staff as well.

A sound basis: a meticulous selection process and initial training

An optimal match between the employee and the job is crucial for sustainable employment. This match is stimulated by the selection process which includes a 'starters' training (different from the training described below) offered by the company. During the initial training period, they work with colleagues who speak a different language to stimulate everyone to speak Dutch. The quality of the employees' work is assessed and on their first day they are given a 'task card', which describes all their duties, including health and safety aspects. The manager has a form where (s)he writes down which tasks the new employees have completed as part of their initial training. At the end of the week this form is sent to the personnel department, which arranges a meeting with the new employees. The personnel officer explains the company's staff rules and goes through the form with the employees to ensure they understand its contents.

Training policy

All employees, including the office staff, have to obtain a basic certificate 'Skilled Cleaner'. During the training sessions they are taught not only to clean to high standards, but also how to relate to customers and colleagues. Trainees also learn about their own rights and responsibilities in the field of occupational safety and health. They are made aware of safety and health-related risks in their job and learn how to deal with these risks.

Because language often appears to be an obstacle to perform the job efficiently and safely, employees are also offered Dutch language courses. This enables them to understand important job instructions such as the use of personal protective equipment when using dangerous cleaning products. In general, most employees do not object to attending the basic course. Convincing them of the importance of a language course seems to be more difficult, however. The head of the personnel department tries to illustrate the importance of a language course by presenting familiar problem situations: 'Do you have children? How do you talk to their teacher? How will you speak to your doctor once your children leave home?' This approach has been successful in persuading workers to attend the language course.

The employer covers the training costs, the extra hours of work and the expenses, asking the employee for commitment and time in return. Approximately 80 % of the employees have completed this basic training. The target is 85–95 %.

Occupational safety and health policy

The employer is responsible for the safety, health and well-being of his/her employees and of the staff of third parties, visitors and consumers of products and services. The company takes its responsibility very seriously, and therefore attempts to reduce the risk of physical or mental injury as much as possible.

No one is called on to perform dangerous or harmful work. When circumstances do not make it possible to eliminate all dangerous work, risks are identified, analysed and minimised. This occupational safety and health approach is integrated in the training policy (see above).

Absenteeism policy

The absenteeism policy aims to improve the performance of both the employees and the company in general, by teaching cleaners how to balance the demands of work and private life to avoid poor performance at work and taking unjustified sick leave. (Employees often report sick when they are experiencing practical household problems, for example, lack of childcare). Managers have been trained to make discreet enquiries when someone calls in sick.

To avoid abuse, the absenteeism policy has become stricter, and employees are given limited chances to make up for misconduct. The absenteeism policy has been very successful; the absentee rate in 2004 was just 3.3 %, which is very low for a cleaning company.

Development discussions

In 2004 MAS introduced 'development discussions' for employees who have been with the company for a year or more — a very unusual practice in the cleaning sector. Managers and workers are helped by the human resources department, which draws up a list of areas of improvement for all employees.

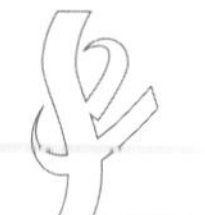

In theory, employees are allowed to discuss the good aspects of their job and suggest areas for improvement of their managers and the company, but, in practice, they are afraid to do so. Being able to speak to the personnel officer rather than their direct boss makes it easier for them to do this. These discussions give employees and the employer the opportunity to evaluate work satisfaction, and as a result hopefully to increase well-being at work.

Participation

MAS believes it is important for employees to have their say, but a proposed employees' council failed due to lack of interest. Therefore, a different type of participation was devised. Every two months a different group of employees from the company's various levels is invited to a meeting. They receive a letter at home asking them to take part in this discussion meeting. They receive the agenda and they can add points for discussion. When taking part in the meeting, they are paid normal working hours. More and more employees are enthusiastic about this initiative and want to participate. The topics are diverse, from practical arrangements during Ramadan to the start of a new training programme. These meetings resulted in better insights into bottlenecks and higher employee participation.

Rewarding

Commitment and dedication are amply rewarded at MAS. Every year employees who performed well are rewarded, and workers who have obtained a diploma or certificate or have been working at MAS for a long time also receive additional benefits. This has a positive effect on workers' motivation. The company pays up to 7.5 % above the wage stipulated in the collective labour agreement. Consequently, MAS's staff policy is not cheap, but this is partly compensated for by the advantages of the company's efficient policy. MAS's low absenteeism allows the company to reduce costs. Moreover, the company does not need to spend any money on recruiting new employees, as it is easy to find candidates through word of mouth. The company has a lower profit margin than the average cleaning company, but this has not caused any problems as MAS's turnover is increasing by 30 % a year.

4.11.3. Results and evaluation of the project

Thanks to Rahma el Mouden's philosophy and approach, MAS has become a successful company with well-trained and motivated employees whose work is of a high standard. An additional result of the company's efficient staff policy is the low absenteeism, which stands at less than 4 %. Thanks to its good reputation, MAS has no recruitment expenses. Candidates either apply spontaneously or they are recruited through the company's current employees. MAS's employees have the opportunity for promotion, for example to specialised cleaners, supervisors or unit managers.

In 2004 MAS joined forces with Investors in People. MAS was the first cleaning company in the Netherlands to be awarded the Investors in People (http://www.iipnl.nl) quality mark. Every year an external audit is carried out in addition to the four annual internal audits MAS carries to analyse whether the new activities have produced the desired effect.

4.11.4. Problems faced

One potential pitfall with training staff in the cleaning industry is that, due to the high turnover of workers, they might leave soon after being trained and enable one's competitors to benefit from the training. In fact, MAS has not found this to be a problem. Thanks to the company's investment in their workers' personal development, employees are loyal and do not leave as readily as in other cleaning companies. When staff do move on, they are good ambassadors for MAS in their next job.

4.11.5. Success factors

MAS's approach has succeeded thanks to the following factors.

- Policy is an integrated one that encourages employees to adopt a positive attitude towards training.
- The importance of training within MAS is highlighted right from the interview stage.
- The training process is systematic so that employees get used to having their performance discussed. This is particularly important when teaching employees new tasks.
- The company can draw on its own experience when motivating employees to take up training, because its workforce consists mainly of immigrants.
- Training hours are paid as working hours.
- Attention is paid to language and to proficiency in Dutch.
- There is a focus on work-life balance, and formulating satisfactory solutions to problems in collaboration with the employees.
- The staff policy is adequately funded.
- Attention is paid to possible cultural differences.

4.11.6. Transferability of the project

This success story proves that investing in employee training and development yields dividends. Trusting and respecting workers generates loyalty towards the company and high levels of motivation.

Investing in employees pays in the long run, regardless of industry. Instead of focusing solely on the employees' shortcomings, such as not having a thorough command of a language, companies should focus on their employees' willingness to learn and their potential.

4.11.7. Details of initiative

Table 60: Multicultural Amsterdam Cleaning company

Title	MAS Dienstverleners (Multicultural Amsterdam Cleaning Company)
Type of project	A diversity policy through an extensive staff policy
Lead organisation	MAS Dienstverleners
Contact information	MAS Dienstverleners Pieter Braaijweg 107-109, 1099 DK Amsterdam, NETHERLANDS Jan Makenbach, operational director Tel. +31 206174926, Fax +31 206698051 E-mail: jan@mas-dienstverleners.nl http://www.masdienstverleners.nl
Date of project	1997–ongoing
References	Smit A.A. et al. 'Lager opgeleiden in beweging: Employability van lager opgeleiden, aanbevelingen en praktijkvoorbeelden', TNO, 2005, pp. 78–84[101]. 'Diversiteitsbeleid heeft iconen nodig', A+O Magazine 11, Maart 2007, pp. 20–21 [102]. Passenier P. 'Personeel is keizer; Schoonmaakbedrijf streeft naar beste personeelsbeleid in de branche', Arbo Informatie, 2004.

4.12. Experiences from a government procurement service (Austria)

- BeschaffungsService Austria (Procurement Service Austria) provides procurement guidelines and advice to all government and public institutions
- The institute has issued a guideline (Module 8) on cleaning services
- The focus is mainly on the environment, but social aspects are also considered
- Occupational safety and health issues such as skin protection are included
- Experiences from Vienna hospitals and schools are presented

4.12.1. Introduction

BeschaffungsService Austria develops procurement guidelines in close cooperation with all stakeholders. Particular attention is paid to ensuring that the tools developed are legally sound and products and services in public tenders are described correctly. This is important because purchasers must avoid allegations that they are acting against national and EU regulations.

101 Available in Dutch (http://www.leren-werken.nl/html/documenten/tnorapport_lageropgeleidenin-beweging_sept2005.pdf).

102 Available in Dutch (http://www.aeno.nl/fileadmin/Organisatie/Documenten/AenO_Magazine_11def.pdf).

Governmental and public authorities can then make use of these guidelines, covering both selection criteria and awarding procedures, but they are free to adapt them as necessary. Reports on how the scheme is applied are published on a regular basis.

4.12.2. Aims and objectives

The main task of BeschaffungsService Austria is to provide advice for purchasers, in the form of guidelines and information. The aim is to change the public procurement field by persuading professionals that good purchasing also means environmentally and socially sound purchasing. Municipalities can play a leading role in environmental and health protection. They are large-scale consumers of detergents and thus have the ability to reduce pollution caused by these agents, as well as to ameliorate their impact on the health of cleaning staff, not least when it comes to skin diseases [103].

4.12.3. Scope of the project — what was done

The general approach is to influence the providers of products and services by specifying 'greener' and more sustainable procurement criteria for governmental and public institutions. To this end BeschaffungsService Austria develops procurement guidelines in close cooperation with all stakeholders. These guidelines are published in the so-called 'Check-it!' catalogue.

Cleaning services are covered under module 8 (Cleaning). The aim of this module is to promote healthier and more environmentally friendly cleaning practices; it is not meant to be a handbook on cleaning. Chapter 3 addresses skin protection and occupational safety and health in detail. The following information is included.

- Skin diseases were at the top of the list of occupational illnesses in Austria up to 1996. Since then protection measures seem to have had some impact and they have fallen to second place.
- Methods of skin protection are explained in detail, for example:
    - avoiding contact with dangerous chemicals or replacing them with less dangerous products and/or applying them mechanically;
    - avoiding skin contact during wet work;
    - wearing appropriate gloves (see AUVA [104] for a detailed list);
    - making special gloves available for allergy sufferers.
- The legal requirements of the ArbeitnehmerInnen-Schutzgesetz (Workers Protection Law) are explained, including the duties of the employer and the employee, the need for proper instructions and the necessity to wear appropriate personal protection equipment (PPE).
- Safety and health measures when working with disinfectants.

In general the guideline states that when tenders are invited for contracts, the contractors should be expected to fulfil environmental and social criteria so that the best bid, not necessarily the cheapest bid, wins the contract [105]. The guidelines

103 From a short version for procurement officials, Module 5: Cleaning, unpublished, available in PDF format from BeschaffungsService Austria.

104 The AUVA is the Austrian Social Insurance for Occupational Risks and provides a wide range of information online (http://www.auva.at).

105 Module 5, see note 103.

indicate how tender specifications can be established and what the intended contract might look like. The annex contains a list of substances that are banned from cleaning agents used in contracts.

4.12.4. Results and evaluation of the project

The HTL Donaustadt [106] school in Vienna applied the procurement guide in a cleaning service tender. The tender included certain environmental criteria and stipulated an hourly work rate calculated by the safety and health department. Fourteen companies bid for the tender, and their reaction was positive.

The Vienna Krankenanstaltenverbund [107] (hospital association) started restructuring its procurement practice in 1992. Six years later a new tender was set up for the purchase of cleaning agents without the ingredients on the above mentioned list. Bidders were also asked to use microfibre cloth. These have a high capillary suction and therefore absorb a lot of dirt without the need for much water or chemicals. It is even possible to use them without any liquid at all. Thus bidders were asked to considerably reduce their wet processes.

4.12.5. Challenges and successes

A challenge faced was that applying occupational safety and health standards within the guidelines of BeschaffungsService Austria had rarely been done before, so the two organisations had little practical experience to build on. The comprehensive approach and the careful development, bearing in mind the European legislation, can be considered as success factors.

4.12.6. Transferability of the project

As BeschaffungsService Austria is careful not to violate European law, institutions in other Member States are not likely to face problems in applying this scheme and/or making use of the guidelines and practices. The guidelines are available in English and German.

106 Donaustadt website (http://www.htl-donaustadt.at).

107 Wiener Krankenanstaltenverbund website (http://www.wienkav.at).

4.12.7. Details of initiative

Table 61: Experiences from procurement service Austria

Title	Experiences from BeschaffungsService Austria (Procurement Service Austria)
Type of project	Development and application of procurement guidelines Experience with procurement guidelines
Focus	Public procurement
Lead organisation	BeschaffungsService Austria
Contact person	BeschaffungsService Austria Dr Ines Öhme, IFZ Graz, Schlögelgasse 2, 8010 Graz, AUSTRIA Tel. +43 3168139099, Fax +43 316810274 E-mail: beschaffung@ifz.tu-graz.ac.at
Further information	EU-OSHA — European Agency for Safety and Health at Work Occupational safety and health in marketing and procurement 2001 http://osha.europa.eu/publications/reports/304/index.htm BeschaffungsService Austria on the website of IFZ http://www.ifz.tugraz.at/index.php/article/articleview/19/1/9/

4.13. Safety and security for cleaners — Dussmann Service (Austria)

- Enterprise level intervention looking particularly at psychosocial and musculo-skeletal loads

4.13.1. Introduction

A project called 'Gesunde und sichere Reinigung', focusing on cleaning workers, was carried out by Dussmann-Service Austria, a major facilities management company, in cooperation with the Lower Austrian Worker's Chamber[108], the AUVA (Austrian Social Insurance for Occupational Risks), Fund for a Healthy Austria[109] and NÖ Gebietskrankenkasse NÖGKK (Lower Austria Regional Health Insurance).

The project was based on a three-year awareness campaign within the company. It arose from earlier prevention research projects[110] that brought about valuable insights into health and safety problems faced by cleaners, as well as concerted efforts by important stakeholders including workers, doctors, workers' representatives and health insurance specialists. The situation of the cleaning personnel was analysed thoroughly and it became clear that cleaners are working under enormous physical

108 Arbeiterkammer NÖ — AKNÖ.

109 Fonds Gesundes Österreich — FGÖ.

110 See Huth E. et al., Gesundheitsförderung im Krankenhausbetrieb, Gestaltung Gesunder Artbeitsbedingungen, Projekt Reinigung; Krueger D. et al., 'Risk Assessment and Preventive Strategies in Cleaning Work'.

and psychosocial stress leading to musculoskeletal, as well as cardiovascular and skin diseases caused by complex interrelated conditions. In several working groups intervention measures were developed, discussed, tested and finally applied. In all working groups the cleaners themselves played a large role. Gradually with increasing research and experience the following recommendations were developed.

- Job enrichment is of importance for the prevention of health problems in the sense that highly strenuous work is frequently interrupted by physically less demanding tasks.
- Teamwork can also help in enabling physically demanding tasks to be alternated with less demanding tasks and it can help to expose cleaners to a greater variety of tasks. Thus it also improves the generally fairly low self-perception of cleaners. Sometimes the ability to work in a team is not well developed and it requires training and qualifications.
- Cleaning should take place at reasonable hours. This helps to coordinate communication, and reduces difficulties such as the need to find childcare at unsocial hours, travelling at night, etc.
- Mop holders should have a standing aid, so there is no need to bend down to pick up fallen mops. Mops should have a parabolic shape, aiding ergonomic movements and handles should be extendable so they can be adjusted to the individual needs of the cleaners.
- Cleaning trolleys meeting ergonomic requirements can reduce carrying of heavy loads and bending.
- For larger areas a battery-powered machine should be considered, which is generally much more efficient than manual cleaning and needs much less physical effort on the part of cleaners. Usually the cleaned area is left dry, thus also reducing the accident risk.
- Floors should be cleaned with dry or damp procedures or there should be a combination of wet and dry methods.
- Washed mops and cloths could be delivered in damp state, which could save water and chemicals and prevent wet work as well as carrying of heavy buckets. They should have a higher content of synthetic materials.
- Clothes should provide adequate protection but should also meet the expectations of the cleaners in terms of wearability and style. In some cases, women felt humiliated by the clothes they had to wear. A smart and well-designed outfit adds remarkably to an increased self-perception of the personnel.
- Shoes should be closed in the rear at order to give sufficient support and they should have a special sole to prevent slips.
- A skin protection plan should be in force, starting with the selection of appropriate gloves, and taking into account factors such as sweating under damp tight materials. Protective emollients and gels should be used if necessary.
- Cleaners seldom attend training courses, for a number of reasons. Cleaners need realistic opportunities for advancement and they need specially designed courses e.g. national language, preparing for school leaver certificates and vocational training certificates, before feeling that they will benefit from the qualification.
- Health and safety training is also needed and should also be designed specifically for the target group. Cleaners often have considerable practical experience in their trade but on the other hand have a low perception of their job and often a low educational status. Qualification and training concepts should consider this, e.g. build on their practical experience, be practice-oriented and have a slow and sensible approach to learning situations.

- 'Moving with Awareness' (developed by Professor Elke Huth)[111] is a method of moving ergonomically while working with mops, brooms, vacuum cleaners, cloths, etc. It was developed in collaboration with cleaning workers and other experts.
- Qualifications are also needed for superiors, managers, and other stakeholders to raise their awareness of the problems cleaning workers are confronted with and to introduce the methods to overcome them. They also have to reconsider their social recognition of cleaning workers, as cleaning becomes a more and more important task in our society.
- Constructive measures such as the installation of floor coverings with compacted surfaces (to which dirt will not stick), enough space for cleaning procedures, wallpaper, furniture and fabrics that do not attract dirt, small baseboards (dirt cannot settle on top), etc.

4.13.2. Aims and objectives

During the two-year project a company awareness-building scheme will be developed. At the company's Hainburg and Hollabrunn sites 90 employees, including managers, will take part. The general aim is to prevent occupational illnesses and at the same time enhance the workers' satisfaction. Workers such as cleaners, kitchen staff and managers will be put in a position to gradually take over more and more responsibility, by establishing the implications of their activities in common learning processes. This will enhance their self-esteem.

Special objectives are:

- reduction of sick leave and absenteeism;
- enhancement of work satisfaction and well-being;
- reduction of physical and psychological stress factors;
- improvement of safety and health consciousness of the employees;
- prevention of occupational illnesses;
- environmental protection improvements;
- development of structures to allow employees to participate in designing work processes;
- integration of health, environment and safety into the corporate identity and into the management system.

4.13.3. Scope of the project — what was done

The general approach is awareness-raising, because, from the experience of other projects, it has become clear that to improve the situation of cleaning workers it is necessary to make them part and parcel of the ongoing activities. Therefore their representatives will be members of the project steering committee and the cleaners themselves will be an important part of the health circles.

The project started with a meeting at both company sites (see picture above), followed by employees' interviews. After the results have been published, work groups (health circles) will evaluate the survey. There are two health circles at each company site. These will meet and develop suggestions on shortcomings which need

111 See Huth, Elke, Moving with Awareness – An Ergonomic Approach to Training Cleaning Personnel, undated, unpublished, and also (http://www.bewegungs-abc.de).

to be addressed. They will also prepare training courses on healthy living topics such as skincare and diet.

The training concept 'Moving with Awareness' will also be presented and trained personnel will, in turn, train all employees of the company. The other topic, which will be addressed in detail, is job enrichment and teamwork. Based on the findings of earlier projects by Professor Krueger, measures will be introduced to reduce strenuous work by 'blending' it with less physically demanding tasks.

The project will also look into the way cleaners are introduced to their job. It is not uncommon in the cleaning sector for new staff to receive only short instructions, often by fellow workers, if any at all. Professor Elke Huth has found that these workers are more often sick or remain in the job for a short period only [112]. The two company site managers will come up with a way of giving staff a proper introduction to the job. Finally, the prevention of drug addiction will also be addressed. Where necessary, it is also planned to purchase ergonomically sound equipment such as telescopic broom and mop handles and an integrated cleaning system.

The project will cost about EUR 140 000 and will end in December 2008, but it is envisaged that the steering committee and the health circle will continue their work to achieve a continuous improvement process.

4.13.4. Results and evaluation of the project

The survey results of the written interviews of the workforce regarding their work conditions and health problems will be published in a so-called first health report. No fewer than 72 % of the employees filled out the questionnaires. After the health circles have analysed the data and developed appropriate measures, the steering committee will check these strategies and plan their implementation. Afterwards there will be a control survey to see whether the desired results have been achieved.

The project will be evaluated by the department of occupational psychology of the AMZ (Arbeitsmedizinisches Zentrum — Centre for occupational medicine) Mödling in form of a result and a process evaluation.

4.13.5. Success factors and transferability

The intense three years of preparation by the workers' council is likely to prove to be one of the success factors of the project. Another positive aspect is the involvement of the cleaning workers into the development of the preventive measures. This will guarantee that the measures can and will be applied in practice because all relevant employees and managers will identify with the project and will back it up. Following its experiences, the company feels that this project could be transferred to all cleaning service providers and it is considering implementing it in all its Austrian sites.

112 Cited in Projektbeschreibung, BGF-Projekt Dussmann, 2007, p. 24.

4.13.6. Details of initiative

Table 62: GSR

Title	GSR (Gesunde und sichere Reinigung) — Dussmann Service
Type of project	Prevention project Surveys, measures developed by health circles
Focus	Cleaning sector
Lead organisation	Dussmann Service [113]
Contact person	Dussmann Service Susanne Deimel-Heiderer, project manager Inzersdorf 95, 3130 Herzogenburg, AUSTRIA Tel. +43 6645055903 E-mail: deimel-heiderer@wien.dussmann.at Professor Elke Huth, Baron-Voght-Str. 202, 22607 Hamburg, GERMANY Tel. +49 40826518 E-mail: elkehuth@gmx.net
Other organisation(s) involved	Arbeiterkammer NÖ — AKNÖ (Worker's Chamber Lower Austria) AUVA (Austrian Social Insurance for Occupational Risks) Fond Gesundes Österreich — FGÖ (Fund for a Healthy Austria) NÖ Gebietskrankenkasse- NÖGKK (Regional Health Insurance Lower Austria)
Other partners actively involved	ÖGB (Austrian trade union association) Arbeitsmedizinisches Zentrum Mödling
Date of project	January 2007–December 2008

4.14. Good practice guidelines in a radiopharmaceuticals department (Poland)

- Improving cleaning procedures
- Controlling all cleaning activities which take place in the department of radiopharmaceuticals
- Promoting the philosophy of good practice

4.14.1. Introduction

The Department of Radiopharmaceuticals at the National Medicines Institute was established in 1968 to evaluate the quality of the radiopharmaceuticals manufactured in Poland as well as new radiopharmaceuticals being considered for marketing authorisation in Poland. The Department is located at Radioisotope Centre POLATOM in Otwock-Świerk.

113 See also (http://www.dussmann.at/web/cms/front_content.php?client=1&lang=1&idcat=52&idart=93&m=&s=&selcat=52).

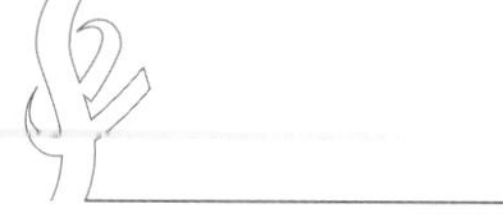

Preparation of radiopharmaceuticals is potentially hazardous because of the radioactivity of the products involved. The level of risk depends on the types of radiation emitted. Particular attention must be paid to the prevention of cross-contamination, to the retention of radionuclide contaminants, and to waste disposal.

Even if the number of staff working in the area where radioactive products are handled is small, all operations need to be carried out under the control of a clearly identified responsible person. All personnel in the radiopharmaceutical department, including those responsible for cleaning, should receive additional training specific to this class of product. The training should be appropriate to the tasks performed.

The main type of radiation in nuclear medicine practice is classed as ionising radiation. The objective of radiation safety is to reduce public and occupational exposure to a minimum. Radiation protection and safety at any radiopharmaceutical production facility is concerned with the protection of all employees including cleaning personnel.

This case study shows how cleaning is organised in a Polish radiopharmaceutical department and is a good example of complex cleaning procedures put into practice. The instructions and approved cleaning procedures are described. These documents specify:

- the responsibilities for cleaning operations;
- the schedule of cleaning;
- the area to be cleaned;
- the steps to be taken during any accident;
- the occupational accident reporting system;
- the special equipment and precautions necessary in particular areas of the department.

4.14.2. Aims and objectives

Good practice guidelines were prepared to minimise the ionising radiation risk at the workplace. The aim was to advise all staff involved in the cleaning of laboratories that might be affected by contamination. Specific guidance was given on determining the cleaning methods and frequency.

4.14.3. Scope of the project — what was done

The personnel responsible for quality control and the department of safety and health in the National Medicines Institute have prepared an extensive system of documentation. The system complies with the health and safety standards.

All activities of cleaners employed in radiochemical and radiobiological laboratories in the Department of Radiopharmaceuticals are described in Standard Operating Procedures. These are written and independently approved for each procedure or activity associated with the operations of the department. These authorised written procedures give instructions for performing laboratory cleaning operations as well as instructions for organising the laboratory as a clean and safe workplace.

The documentation includes instructions about maintenance and cleaning. Buildings used in the manufacture of products should be kept in a clean condition and should be free of infestation. All surfaces (walls, floor, tables and furniture) must be made of materials that are easy to clean and disinfect and to decontaminate in the event of a

radioactive spill. The work surfaces should be easily cleaned and brightly lit to make it easy to find any sources that have been dropped. The surfaces of the room where radionuclides are used or stored, such as benches, tables and seats, should be smooth and non-absorbent, so that they can be easily cleaned and decontaminated.

The cleaning workers in nuclear medicine laboratories do not require personal accreditation in radiation protection but should receive additional training specific to this class of products.

The documentation also specifies the training that cleaners in a radiopharmaceutical department should receive. Personnel working in areas where contamination poses a hazard, e.g. clean areas or areas where highly radioactive, toxic, infectious or sensitising materials are handled, should be given specific training by qualified individuals. Newly recruited personnel should receive training appropriate to the duties assigned to them.

4.14.4. Results and evaluation of the project

The adoption of good practice procedures has helped to reduce the radiation risk. There is now clarity on who is responsible for what action concerning health and safety. The institute's training and audit unit prepared health and safety courses helpful for many groups of workers and these have proved particularly helpful.

4.14.5. Transferability of the project

Guidelines of this sort could be prepared by similar institutions, adapted according to the precise nature of their work and the hazards posed by it. However, considerable care would have to be taken to meet relevant national requirements.

4.14.6. Details of initiative

Table 63: Good practice in a radiopharmaceuticals department

Title	Good practice in a radiopharmaceuticals department
Type of project	Guidance
Focus	Guidelines with instructions and approved cleaning procedures for cleaners in radiopharmaceutical laboratories
Lead organisation	National Medicines Institute, Department of Radiopharmaceuticals
Other organisation(s)	Radioisotope Centre POLATOM
Date of project	2003
Contact details	National Medicines Institute, Department of Radiopharmaceuticals Piotr Garnuszek Ph.D. ul. Chełmska 30/34, 00-725 Warsaw, POLAND http://www.il.waw.pl/eng/LI.html

Workplace health and safety instructions for cleaners

Cleaners at the university are exposed to a number of dangerous agents. The occupational health and safety department of the University of Zielona Góra prepared detailed health and safety instructions for cleaning workers employed at the university. These included regulations for the safe handling of chemicals during cleaning, so that the workers' exposure to dangerous substances was reduced.

Instructions were prepared to familiarise cleaners with basic hazards and indicate ways of eliminating them. Instructions are given on levels of training required, use of protective clothing, availability of instruction manuals for equipment used during work, and other requirements. It is also specified that material safety data sheets (MSDS) must be available for any chemicals used so that workers are informed of their dangers and handling precautions that must be taken [1].

1 Further information can be found in Polish online (http://www.adm.uz.zgora.pl/index.php?dzial=AA04&addon=5).

4.15. Daytime cleaning at Sodexho AB (Sweden)

- Improved communication associated with daytime cleaning
- Daytime cleaning associated with a better work-life balance, better self-esteem and greater safety

4.15.1. Introduction

Sodexho AB is one of the leading service companies in Sweden, with more than 7 000 employees working throughout the country either at Sodexho's own offices or elsewhere on about 2 000 client contracts. Sodexho offers a variety of support services to clients in the business community and public sector, including catering and cleaning, caretaking, switchboards and reception, conferences and events, and facility management services.

The main complaint by cleaners working out of office hours is the lack of contact with a manager; they cannot ask questions or alert anyone if there is a technical or safety problem. They also return home at unsociable hours, which can represent a safety risk. Also, working for short periods for different clients decreases worker efficiency, which may represent a cost increase to the client. Working out of normal office hours means that cleaning staff do not have the chance to communicate with the office staff who directly benefit from their services. Cleaners cannot be directly notified of any problem, or even be praised for good work.

Daytime cleaning was found by Sodexho to be the only way to develop a cleaning service into a decent occupation for the employees. Daytime cleaning makes it possible to have full-time personnel with decent wages providing a high-quality service.

4.15.2. Aims and objectives

In the contract with SEB bank headquarters (Stockholm), daytime cleaning has been in effect since the early 1990s. It is recognised that the image of the cleaning industry is an important reason for the high staff turnover and low worker profile in the sector. Cleaners generally do not feel they have a 'real' job as they work outside office hours when no one else is around, in an industry with part-time work, are hourly paid and generally lack long-term career goals.

Work during asocial hours makes communication difficult between the four main parties in office cleaning: the client, the building occupants, the cleaning staff and the service provider. When communication is poor or absent, the effectiveness and efficiency of the service is directly affected. The increase in communication is the main difference between daytime cleaning and traditional cleaning. This is the key benefit of daytime cleaning that was achieved in the contract with SEB bank headquarters.

4.15.3. Scope of the project — what was done

Daytime cleaning requires an intensive training programme for the whole staff, instilling a sense of pride in the contractors' employees and improving quality for the clients. Sodexho cleaners at the SEB offices felt that occupants appreciated their work. The feeling of being trusted and considered important to the smooth running of the office was an important consequence of daytime cleaning. Office workers know the names of the cleaners at SEB; each staff member is well trained to adapt the cleaning of each room according to the occupant's use of the space.

4.15.4. Results and evaluation of the project

Sodexho has enjoyed 98 % worker retention over recent years. This is probably a direct consequence of the job satisfaction daytime cleaning promotes among its staff. Switching to daytime cleaning at SEB promoted communication between staff, operations managers and the building occupants. This increased worker efficiency and reduced the time and effort wasted by the cleaners. An important benefit at SEB was an increase in client recognition concerning cleaning work. Daytime cleaning allows the clients to see the work being done.

An active communication between SEB's own building designers and the cleaning operations manager was achieved through daytime cleaning. Under discussion were the access areas in the building, particularly the appropriate width of the indoor entrance gates. The safe passage of indoor sweepers, polishers, and similar machines, was taken into account, and a standard procedure defined accordingly. This collaboration was a real sign that the image of the industry was lifted, and that cleaning was seen as a quality service in its own right.

4.15.5. Success Factors

The main difference compared with the traditional cleaning system is an increase in communication. Daytime cleaning allows cleaning staff and office staff to relate and

talk to each other about how the job is being done and what can be improved. With daytime cleaning there is direct contact with the client and a visible reason for office staff to care and collaborate in terms of making cleaning faster and more effective.

Daytime cleaning work was seen to provide cleaners with a sense of security — they had a job that could provide them with a stable base, where they felt confident and appreciated for the work being done.

Being paid above the national minimum and monthly instead of weekly or hourly, in the same way office staff would be, allows staff to feel part of the workforce.

Sodexho has a thorough training programme. Some training programmes in Sodexho may involve 3 000 cleaners for more than 40 hours' training.

According to the company, daytime cleaning brings benefits for clients in terms of cost reduction, time saving, a more consistent service and a better response to their requirements. For the contractors it means easier staff recruitment, a more skilled workforce and higher productivity. Daytime cleaning also benefits employees because it results in a better work-life balance, higher wages, better self-esteem and greater security because they are no longer working nights or evenings.

4.15.6. Transferability of the project

Daytime cleaning may be transferred to different work sectors and to different countries. Naturally, differences in legal, social and political conditions must be taken into consideration. Sodexho has considerable experience with daytime cleaning; in the contract with SEB bank headquarters (Stockholm), daytime cleaning has been carried out since the early 1990s.

4.15.7. Contact information and details of initiative

Table 64: Daytime cleaning at Sodexho AB

Title	Daytime cleaning at Sodexho AB
Type of project	Implementation of daytime cleaning in the SEB Bank (Stockholm)
Focus	Cleaning sector
Lead organisation	Sodexho AB
Contact person	Sodexho AB Thor Franzén, Produktchef Städ Västberga Allé 36 A, Box 47620, 117 94 Stockholm, SWEDEN Tel. +46 857885715, Fax +46 857885810 E-mail: thor.franzen@sodexho-se.com http://www.sodexho-se.com
Others involved	SEB Bank Headquarters (Stockholm)
Date of project	Since early 1990s
References	'Seeing the light', *European Cleaning Journal* [114] 'Grand designs for the future', *European Cleaning Journal* [115]

4.16. Cleaning laboratories at the University of Edinburgh (UK)

- Clear guidelines drawn up for lab cleaning
- Guidelines for university managers, supervisors and cleaning staff
- Guidance at a local and organisation level

4.16.1. Introduction

The range and complexity of potential hazards in most laboratory environments means that special provision must be made for the health and safety of cleaning workers. At the University of Edinburgh, cleaning is carried out by the university cleaners or by the service providers. Changes of cleaning staff, including supervisors, are fairly regular — indicating that there may be a need for induction safety information and instruction.

Each university is required to provide adequate information and training to ensure the health and safety of its workers while employees, whether laboratory-based workers or cleaners, also have a responsibility to work safely and in a safe environment.

114 http://www.europeancleaningjournal.com/index.php?option=com_content&task=view&id=219&Itemid=61

115 http://www.europeancleaningjournal.com/index.php?option=com_content&task=view&id=293&Itemid=61

There are three main types of laboratories at the university. The arrangements for cleaning vary on different sites so there was a need to prepare guidance on the cleaning of all types of laboratories.

The guidelines give the instructions and outline approved cleaning procedures. They also specify the responsibilities for cleaning operations and detailed schedules for cleaning, as well as information about the training that all cleaners should receive.

Laboratory staff, and particularly scientific workers, need to be reminded that the next person entering the laboratory could be the cleaner. Similarly, cleaners need to be aware of some of the special work the university undertakes so that they can avoid injuring themselves and others.

Many laboratories at Edinburgh have special rules and regulations which must be obeyed when cleaners are working there. The health and safety department issues guidelines to cleaners along with any specific explanations and instructions required.

The university health and safety department prepared instructions to ensure the safety of cleaners working in the laboratories. The guidance was prepared not only for cleaning staff but also for university managers and supervisors.

4.16.2. Aims and objectives

The action aimed to provide advice to all those involved in the cleaning laboratories that may be affected by contamination, and maximise health protection of cleaners in the workplace. The document describes how the university's laboratories should be cleaned to reduce the dangers of identified and unidentified hazards.

4.16.3. Scope of the project — what was done

There are three different types of laboratories at the university:

- chemical laboratories, where the main hazard is potential exposure to harmful chemicals;
- biological containment laboratories, where the hazards are the same as in chemical labs, but with the added potential for exposure to micro-organisms;
- radiation laboratories, where the hazards are usually as in those described above, with the additional risk of exposure to radioactive material.

Due to the complexity of potential hazards in most laboratory environments the health and safety department prepared special guidance for all cleaners in all types of laboratories.

Guidelines presented by the department were supplemented by the biosafety unit and the radiation protection units. The University Biological Safety Unit is responsible for producing and enforcing regulations relating to the biological laboratories. The Radiation Protection Unit does the same in areas subject to ionising and non-ionising radiation.

The guidance outlines:

- general considerations and specific arrangements for managers and supervisors;
- responsibilities of laboratory personnel;
- provision of information and instruction;
- supervision and monitoring;

- rules for cleaners in laboratories;
- information about different types of hazards.

Generally the system of documentation is divided in three main parts:

- Part One explains the general considerations and specific arrangements for managers and supervisors;
- Part Two is designed for cleaners working in laboratories and can also be issued to relevant staff as a support to the instruction;
- Part Three contains a list of clear rules for laboratory cleaners.

The first section informs managers and supervisors about their duty to provide cleaning staff with relevant information and instruction to enable them to work safely. Managers and university staff are obliged to ensure that cleaners are not put in a position where they have to make a decision whether the laboratory is safe to clean or not. This section also gives detailed information about the specific arrangements which should be made for cleaners working in biological contaminant laboratories or radiation controlled area laboratories.

The later sections of the guidance give a list of 'DOs', 'DO NOTs' and 'IF' for cleaning laboratories. The most important guidelines describe the use of the personal protective equipment, behaviour in the laboratory and the accident reporting system. It also lists sources of further information.

4.16.4. Results and evaluation of the project

The 'Cleaning of laboratories' guidance was prepared not only for cleaners but also for supervisors and managers — which is important because they have responsibility for their employees. University supervisors regularly monitor and review the arrangements in place to ensure that the requirements are being met and cleaners are working safely and effectively. It is difficult to say what impact the guidelines have had because they were only prepared about three years ago; a reduction in occupational diseases and injuries cannot be measured in such a short time.

4.16.5. Problems faced

Laboratories are not 'normal' workplaces, and they contain hazards that put cleaning workers at risk, for example from biological, chemical or radioactive contaminants. Because of this, all cleaners working in biological and radioactive laboratories must receive information, training and supervision appropriate for the work undertaken, so that risks to the health and safety of all persons involved are controlled. This includes awareness-raising of the dangers present in the laboratories and what should and should not be done as part of the cleaning routine. Care had to be taken during the provision of information and training to the cleaning workers as not all were fluent in English.

It was found that individual cleaning staff changes, without the prior knowledge of the laboratory manager, made it difficult to manage the information provision, training, and supervision of the cleaning workers. As a result, cleaning workers are excluded from certain areas where the contamination risk is high and the cleaning activities in these locations are carried out either by laboratory staff or by cleaning staff under the direct supervision of the laboratory manager following a risk assessment.

Finally, it was found that laboratory workers needed to be reminded that they also had a responsibility for the cleanliness at their own workstations.

4.16.6. Success factors

The use of the guidance improves communication. It means that cleaners, managers and all laboratory staff are obliged to work together to minimise potential hazards in workplace. It also helps to promote the philosophy of good practice in the laboratories. If the guidance is applied, work-related ill health and injuries suffered by cleaners will be reduced.

4.16.7. Transferability of the project

Drawing up similar guidelines on cleaning could be appropriate for other institutions such as schools and hospitals which have their own laboratories. The guidance could also be used by other service providers.

The University of Edinburgh guidelines have been adapted for use at the College of Medicine and Veterinary Medicine.

4.16.8. Details of initiative

Table 65: Cleaning of laboratories at the University of Edinburgh

Title	Cleaning of laboratories at the University of Edinburgh
Type of project	Guidance for cleaners and management
Focus	To provide advice on occupational safety and health to all those involved in the cleaning of laboratories that may be affected by contamination
Lead organisation	University of Edinburgh
Contact person	The University of Edinburgh — Health and Safety Department John Adamson, Occupational Hygiene and Safety Adviser Charles Stewart House, 9–16 Chambers, Edinburgh, EH1 1HT, UK E-mail: John.Adamson@ed.ac.uk http://www.safety.ed.ac.uk/ContactUs/showcontacts.cfm
Date of project	2005

European Agency for Safety and Health at Work

WORKING ENVIRONMENT INFORMATION

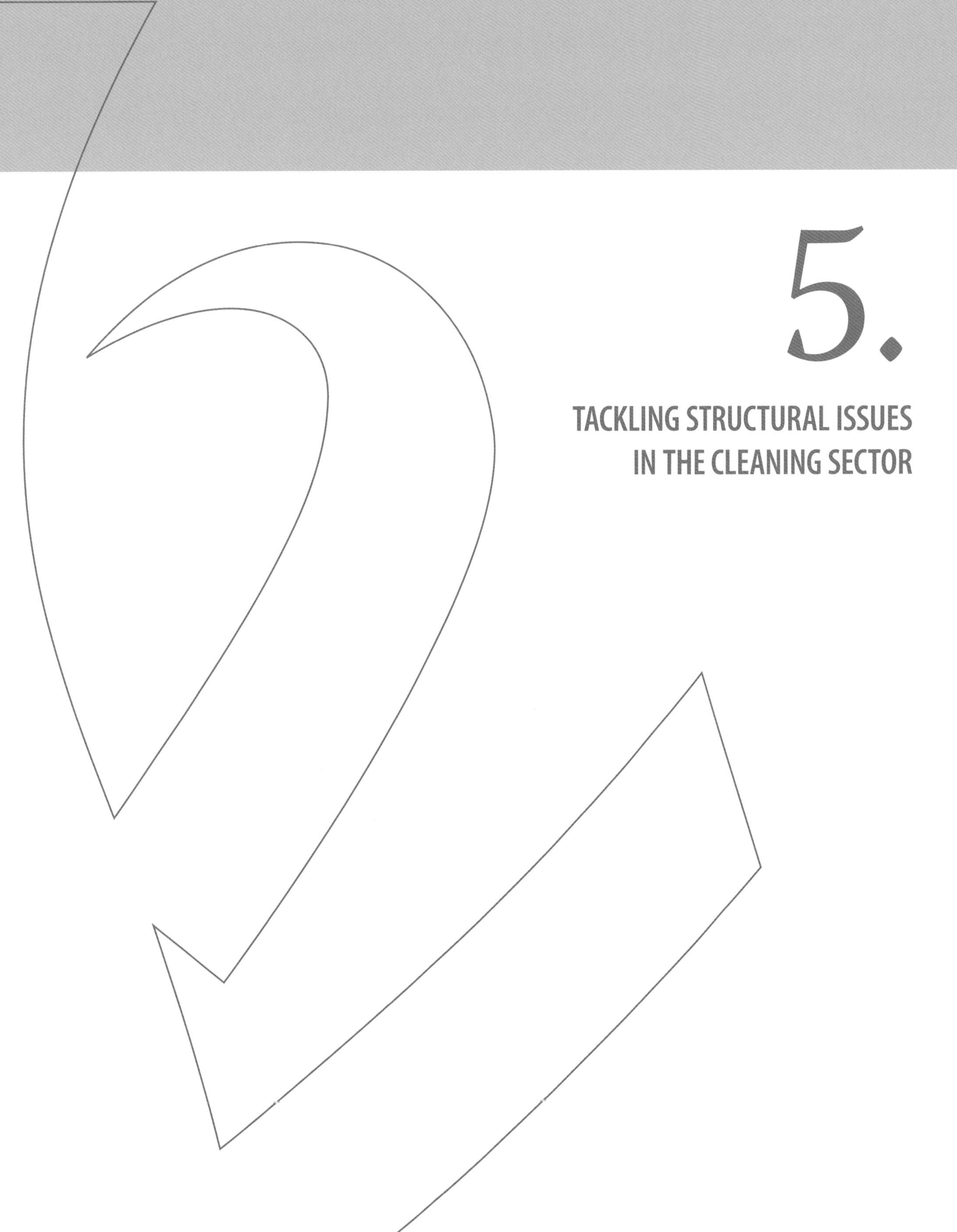

5.

TACKLING STRUCTURAL ISSUES IN THE CLEANING SECTOR

The cleaning industry is one of the largest and most dynamic service sectors in the European Union. Rapidly developing technological processes require rapidly developing maintenance and cleaning procedures.

However, the sector suffers from the low public perception of cleaning and its association with dirt and waste. This is aggravated by various levels of outright discrimination which, according to a German union official, are widespread: failure to pay the minimum wage and adhere to agreed conditions of service; sexual harassment and violence at the workplace; non-compliance with occupational safety and health provisions; discrimination based on ethnic origin [116]. All of these are interrelated and lead not only to direct physical injuries but also to stress-related health problems. The implementation of preventive measures needs a holistic approach.

But the good news is that employers, employees and authorities have taken up the challenge. There are numerous interventions planned or under way by individual social partners, or in a combined effort or even as a tripartite initiative. Various institutes, health and accident insurers as well as consultants are also giving valuable inputs.

The structural challenges that adversely affect the occupational safety and health of cleaning workers require action by employers' organisations, unions, inspectorates and expert institutions to ensure that the knowledge of challenges and solutions is disseminated to employers to workers. There is no single method of addressing the issues raised in this report. All need to be involved in finding solutions.

Initiatives at policy level to improve the health and safety of cleaners not only follow the usual tracks of occupational safety and health but also address issues like workload, working time and schedules, work organisation, communication, qualification, career opportunities, and work satisfaction.

By improving the health and safety of their workers, companies benefit in terms of improved image as well as having healthier, self-confident and well-qualified staff. They also prosper in economic terms:

- health problems and absenteeism are reduced;
- appropriate machinery and equipment is introduced, making the work more efficient and effective;
- increased worker retention keeps experience in the company and assures the quality of work;
- effective work organisation is implemented;
- acknowledgement of cleaners greatly enhances their motivation.

116 Arhan Virdi, 'A Victim at Work?' in European Cleaning Journal (http://www.europeancleaningjournal.com/index.php?option=com_content&task=view&id=289&Itemid=61).

Addressing unfair competition and the informal economy

5.1.

The European Federation of Cleaning Industries, EFCI has found evidence of the proliferation of 'cowboy' companies that do not respect their obligations in relation to collective agreements and social security legislation. Such companies often charge prices that do not even cover labour costs, thereby pushing law-abiding companies out of the market[117]. The result is that cleaners pay not only by putting up with low wages and job insecurity, but also by working under unsafe and unhealthy conditions.

5.1.1. Protecting workers and companies through good procurement

A procurement process based on value rather than price is the most important step towards ensuring strong competition among law-abiding enterprises that does not lead to the exposure of cleaning workers to workplace risks. Selection procedures should be based on the economically most advantageous tender rather than on lowest price. Put simply, the cheapest is not always the right choice, as cheap bids may expose the selecting body to higher economic costs overall. Those carrying out the procurement should follow an objective system of quality criteria including health and safety considerations, to identify the best-value bid.

Structural initiatives on this issue can encourage enterprises to take a 'value not price' approach to procurement. As a legislative approach to procurement practice, there exist European Directives 2004/17/EC (the Utilities Directive) and 2004/18/EC (the Classic Directive). The first regulates contracting of works, supplies and services by utilities in the water, energy, transport and postal services sectors, the second contracting by all other public authorities. These allow social considerations to be taken into account in the procurement process but do not provide extensive guidance on this issue.

There is a campaign for good procurement practice 'Making the most of public money' by the Social Platform, an association of over 30 European non-governmental organisations, federations and networks in the social sector. The platform groups started a campaign at Member State level to urge governments and public authorities to include social, ethical and environmental considerations in public procurement processes.

Procurement guides for employers exist that promote responsible forms of procurement and contain a variety of possible criteria and related awarding procedures which can help organisations to choose the best cleaning service organisation. The guidelines also specify what a contract should look like and how tender specifications can be established. Two examples of such guides are the CARPE guide from EUROCITIES Stockholm and the guidelines from Procurement Service Austria. The latter provides detailed instructions on occupational skin protection,

117 European Federation of Cleaning Industries (EFCI) and UNI-Europa Selecting best value — A guide for organisations awarding contracts for cleaning services, 2004, p.11, priced publication (www.feni.be).

giving information on the problem of skin diseases, possible preventive measures and legal requirements. Guidance is also available from the Association of Public Purchasers in Denmark.

Procurement guidelines not only serve as a tool to determine the best service provider but also provide useful information for the cleaning services themselves. These organisations have to learn from the guidelines and see them as a tool that can help them to provide socially sound services.

There are also European and national standards for the procurement of cleaning services and allowing an objective selection of bids by applying standardised output criteria. Occupational safety and health are not always explicit criteria; nevertheless the standard has a direct influence on the working conditions of cleaners. For example, there is a European standard for cleaning services [118] and a German Standard for the cleaning of school buildings [119]. However, the European Committee on Standardisation, CEN concluded in 2005: 'Taking into account the size of the cleaning industry, further European standards are needed. European standards on the qualification of personnel, on codes of practice or contract drafting could be further developed at the European level' [120].

The German standard sets criteria for the procurement process regarding the quality and the scope of cleaning, taking into account the special requirements in schools. Thus it is ensured that not only price but also quality standards and professionalism have to be considered in the awarding process. Certain onerous working methods or the use of hazardous working materials have to be avoided. A checklist includes many factors that reduce cleaning expenditure as well as the physical load on cleaners. A non-ergonomic layout of premises can lead to increased maintenance costs later on.

There are many tools available to facilitate the procurement process. The CleanNet software aims to ensure the workers have enough time to do their jobs properly. The software also gives accurate information about how much time a cleaning task using a specific method will take in a certain space. CleanNet also calculates necessary manpower to do the work and the costs related to the task.

One of the success factors is that CleanNet is applicable to specific situations and it contains realistic and reproducible data (all measurements are video-monitored; the videos can be studied in the Helsinki University Library). The programme is also easy to use.

5.1.2. Avoiding exploitation by challenging illegal labour

The employment of illegal labour, where companies avoid paying social costs so that they can compete against responsible employers, has an impact on the safety and health of cleaning workers. In addition to putting in place procurement practices, action has been taken to signal that dishonest practices are not acceptable.

118 European standard EN 13549:2001 Cleaning services — Basic requirements and recommendations for quality measuring systems (http://www.cen.eu).

119 IN 77400:2003-09 Reinigungsdienstleistungen — Schulgebäude — Anforderungen an die Reinigung (Cleaning services — School buildings — Requirements for the cleaning).

120 CEN, Final Report on European Commission Programming Mandate M/340 in the Field of Services, available as a PDF document (http://www.cen.eu/cenorm/businessdomains/businessdomains/services/finalreportm340.pdf).

The social partners and the Belgian government made an agreement to send a signal to all stakeholders in the cleaning sector and to battle dishonest competition practices including: using illegal workers or unregistered labour, not complying with regulations or using irregular or bogus contractors. The government and social partners are also hoping to raise the profile of the profession, improving the morale and training standards among cleaners. Similarly, a collective agreement between the social partners in Luxembourg also addresses the issue of clandestine work and dishonest competition and provides an example of another successful intervention strategy.

5.2. Dealing with image and self-perception

Cleaners have to adapt to technological advancements. New materials are introduced at a rapid rate, making cleaning an ever-changing process. Cleaning agents and equipment also follow this trend. Choosing the right chemicals, equipment and procedures is important to guarantee an extended life for buildings, factories, office equipment and furniture and other infrastructure. Cleaning may also take place in areas where sensitive information or dangerous equipment is stored, thus placing particular demands on the skills and integrity of cleaning personnel. Yet the public perception and the self-perception of cleaners remains low. This discourages the effective management of cleaning services by both service provider and client, with a negative impact on worker health and safety. The negative perception may also discourage workers to enter and stay in the industry, leading to a high staff turnover.

Interesting initiatives to improve this situation are represented by two campaigns in the Netherlands (PR campaign — The Cleaner Makes it Possible by the Industrial Relations Board), and a combined photo documentation and exhibition in northern Germany. These activities, changing the perceptions of both the public and the cleaning workers themselves are needed to ensure that cleaners and their work are respected and understood.

5.3. Promoting health and safety management

The management of cleaners' occupational health and safety is a real challenge as there are frequently two companies involved — the client and the service provider. The provision of specific and targeted information and guidelines for employers (and clients), particularly for smaller companies that may not have the resources to employ safety and health professionals, can stimulate improvements in occupational safety and health management systems. Such systems can be beneficial to both the employers (e.g. through reduced absenteeism) and workers (who avoid harm).

5.3.1. Sharing knowledge

In many Member States there are Internet forums, networks, platforms, portals and databases that allow information to be retrieved and questions to be answered. These sources of information stimulate action and ensure that the correct information is obtained and that it is applicable to cleaning businesses. These initiatives include the GISBAU glove database in Germany, Simpags in Italy, the Polish Infoclean.pl portal, and the UK's HSE Cleaners' portal.

5.3.2. Supporting training

Training workers is a particular challenge in the cleaning sector. Training in such issues as manual material handling benefits not only the worker but also the company, reducing the likelihood of lost time through illness and injury. The nature of employment — often part-time at asocial hours — makes training provision difficult. The provision of support to companies and workers who are providing and undergoing training, such as that by ELINYAE in Greece and ISTAS in Spain, has a big impact on preventing harm to cleaning workers. In Denmark, education and training courses are provided for specific groups of workers such as cleaners that have been developed by the social partners in specific sectors.

5.3.3. Raising awareness about hazards, risks and prevention

Employers cannot effectively manage the risks to their workers without knowledge of the hazards, risks, and solutions involved. Many initiatives have developed guidelines for risk assessment in the cleaning sector. There are four different approaches: one from Belgium stressing the participation of the cleaners, one established by the Hamburg labour inspectorate, a Danish one presenting several tools for download and another one from Poland modelled after the relevant ILO datasheet.

These guides make clear the hazards and risks in the workplace, and the consequences of failing to prevent or control them. They show that practical solutions, which are also often simple and cheap, exist to prevent them. For example, solutions to prevent musculoskeletal disorders include extendible handles for mops, ergonomically designed mop frames, and mops with a support to prevent them from falling down.

5.4. Stimulating changes in work organisation

The working patterns of cleaning workers can have a direct effect on their safety and health. Work organisation is an important topic in research projects such as *Risk Assessment and Preventive Strategies in Cleaning Work*[121] and similar studies. These

121 Krueger, Detlef, Louhevaara, Veikko, Nilsen, Jette, Schneider, Thomas (eds), Risk Assessment and Preventive Strategies in Cleaning Work, Werkstattberichte aus Wissenschaft + Technik. Wb 13, Hamburg, 1997. The project is also presented online (http://www.rzbd.fh-hamburg.de/~prbiomed/risk_assessment.html and http://www.ttl.fi/Internet/English/Information/Electronic+journals/Tyoterveiset+journal/1999-02+Special+Issue/06.htm).

projects recommend daytime cleaning, job enrichment, team-based cleaning and more full-time jobs to tackle the sector-specific problems such as the lack of communication between client's employees and cleaners (no feedback, no praise), working alone, and violence to workers.

Encouraging employers and clients to switch to daytime cleaning, which the European Sectoral Social Dialogue Committee for the industrial cleaning sector is doing, can lead to the elimination of risks to cleaners at source.

European Agency for Safety and Health at Work

WORKING ENVIRONMENT INFORMATION

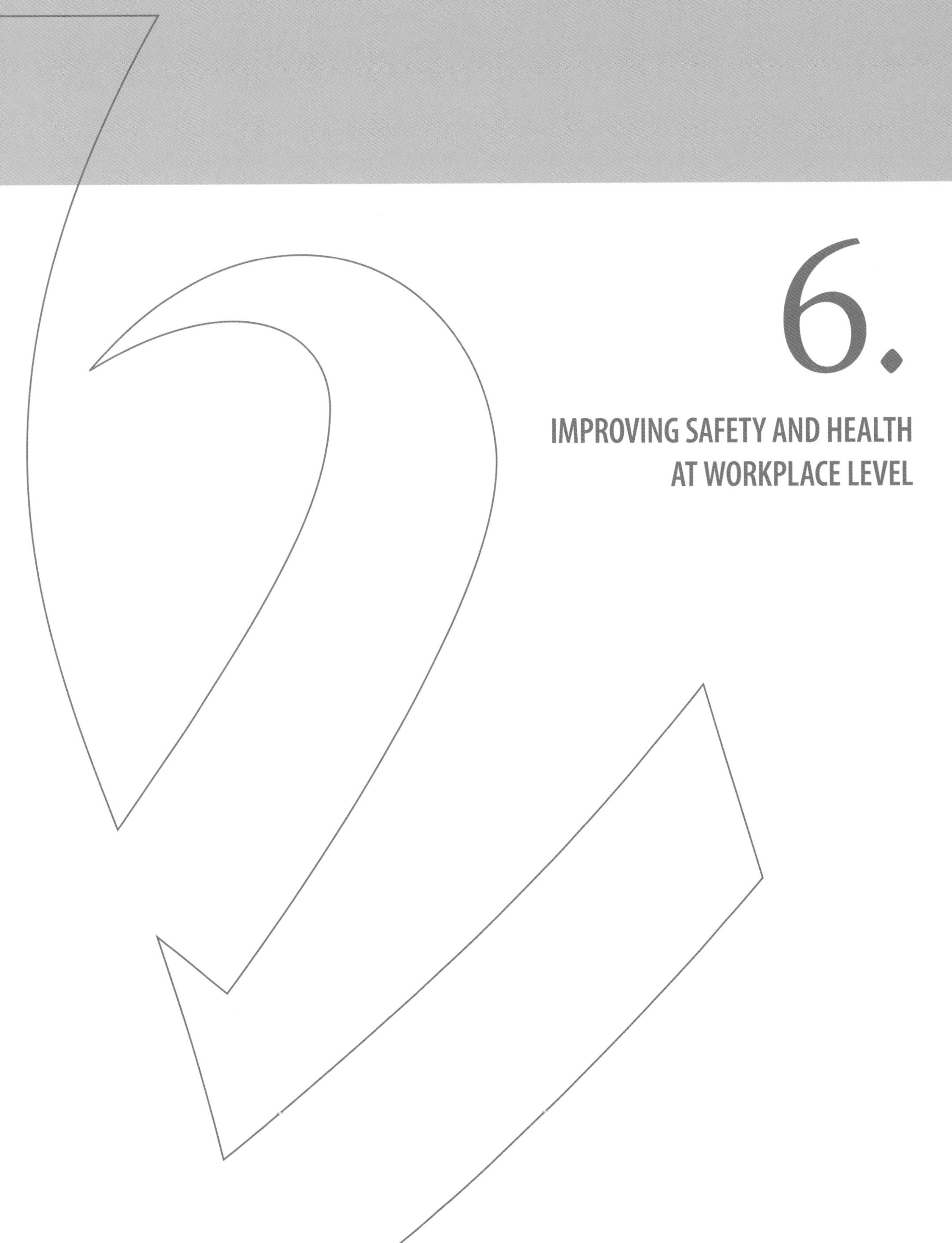

6.

IMPROVING SAFETY AND HEALTH AT WORKPLACE LEVEL

The many initiatives described in this publication show how all stakeholders in the cleaning sector can contribute towards a safe and healthy work environment for cleaners. Good practice derived from these initiatives was used to draw up a list of advice for purchasers and service providers in the cleaning sector when considering tender bids, to create a healthy, safe and stimulating work environment.

By improving the health and safety situation companies benefit in terms of improved image as well as healthier, self-confident and well-qualified staff. They also make economic savings because:

- health problems and absenteeism are reduced;
- appropriate machinery and equipment is introduced, making the work much more effective;
- increased worker retention keeps experience in the company and assures quality of work;
- effective work organisation is implemented;
- acknowledgement of cleaners greatly enhances their motivation.

6.1. Choose the best bidder and not the cheapest when purchasing cleaning services

Employers that purchase cleaning services should contract out these services to the best bidder and not the cheapest. What appears to be cheaper may turn out to be more costly overall. For example, improper cleaning of surfaces can lead to more rapid wear and the resultant need for more frequent replacement or repair, and bad cleaning practice can lead to 'slips' accidents (e.g. through leaving a wet surface) that results in an accident to a worker from the host enterprise with the resulting costs.

6.2. Implement and promote daytime cleaning

The unsocial hours at which cleaners frequently have to work do not encourage people to enter the industry. According to a study by EFCI [122], cleaners usually work outside normal office hours. Morning (6.00–9.00 a.m.), evening (6.00–9.00 p.m.) or night cleaning seems practical because most workers are off duty and offices and factories are thus empty. This means cleaners can get on with their job without disturbing office routine. However, working at unsocial times places heavy demands on the cleaners themselves, in terms of travelling to work, balancing their home life, security, etc.

122 European Federation of Cleaning Industries, The cleaning industry in Europe, an EFCI Survey, 2006 (Data 2003), European Federation of Cleaning Industries (EFCI) (http://www.feni.be).

When planned and organised properly, daytime cleaning can be implemented in such a way as not to interfere with the work routine. Some practical adjustments have to be made and stakeholders need to be well informed about the transition, but it is not an impossible job. The Ministry of Social Affairs and Employment in the Netherlands has successfully introduced daytime cleaning. In order to provide a smooth transition to the new system, the ministry mapped out all the pros and cons. A transition plan was then developed and implemented by a multidisciplinary team, meaning that the purchaser, the cleaning company and the employees from both organisations were represented. The transition plan, which can serve as an example for other organisations, public as well as private, comprised 18 steps.

Daytime cleaning should be promoted wherever possible because it reduces the psychosocial hazards to which the cleaners are exposed. Sodexho Sweden implemented daytime cleaning in the 1990s, and all stakeholders experienced some benefits.

Integrate occupational safety and health management into general management 6.3.

In order to provide a safe and healthy work environment, organisations can implement an occupational health and safety management system. Several institutes provide these kinds of systems. Such a system should be integrated in the overall policy so that a comprehensive approach is possible, and it should fit the corporate culture so that employees feel involved.

Investing in such systems sends a message to the employees, namely that the management is motivated to invest in the safety and health of their workers. It is important to involve the cleaners in the development and implementation of such a system.

An example of an occupational safety and health management system in the cleaning sector is AMS BAU, an action plan comprising 11 stages towards safe and economic cleaning work. The plan offers a way to manage safety and health issues in an effective, well-organised manner. This means that an occupational health and safety policy should be at the basis of all decisions and actions concerning the topic. Effective organisation also means proper communication towards the employees about health and safety issues. Employees will feel that their boss cares about them and as a result a climate of confidence will be created.

Within the framework of the occupational safety and health system, cleaning procedures can be developed for the different tasks of the job. These procedures might explain how to clean in a safe and healthy way. It is important that these instructions and approved cleaning procedures are well described. Responsibility for cleaning operators, schedules, area to be cleaned, steps to be taken in the event of an accident, the occupational accident reporting system, special requirements and precautions necessary in particular areas of the department are also covered.

6.4. Identify the risks and set up effective preventive measures

It is the responsibility of the cleaner's employer to identify and evaluate the possibility of harm to each worker, and the preventive measures required to prevent the harm or, if this is not possible, to reduce the risk that it might occur. This process is called risk assessment [123].

The goal of the risk assessment process is to identify all risks to the workers, and to install effective measures to protect them. To protect cleaning workers from accidents and ill health, it is important that the employer works out prevention and intervention strategies adapted to each different workplace or work area.

Employers have a legal obligation to protect the health and safety of their workforce. The employer must evaluate the risks for safety and health within the workplace(s) and then improve the standards of safety and health for all workers (and any others) who may be harmed. If employees of two employers work together, the employers must coordinate the work.

A good risk assessment should, therefore, form the basis for the selection of work equipment and cleaning detergents, personal protective measures, the training of the workforce and the organisation of the work in collaboration with the owner or operator of the premises to be cleaned. It should cover all standard operations and it should reflect how the work is carried out. To make sure that all aspects of the job are considered, the workers should be involved in the risk assessment process.

123 See EU-OSHA — European Agency for Safety and Health at Work E-fact 36 — Prevention of accidents and ill health to cleaners 2008 (http://osha.europa.eu/en/publications/e-facts/efact36/view).

Table 66: Five steps to risk assessment

Five steps to risk assessment	
1 — Identifying hazards and those at risk	Looking for those things at work that have the potential to cause harm, and identifying workers who may be exposed to the hazards.
2 — Evaluating and prioritising risks	Estimating the risks (their severity, their probability, etc.) and prioritising them in order of importance. It is essential that any work that needs to be done to eliminate or prevent risks is prioritised.
3 — Deciding on preventive action	Identifying the appropriate measures to eliminate or control the risks.
4 — Taking action	Putting in place the preventive and protective measures through a prioritisation plan (it is unlikely that all problems can be resolved immediately) and specifying who does what and when, and the means allocated to implement the measures.
5 — Monitoring and reviewing	The assessment should be reviewed at regular intervals to ensure it remains up to date. It has to be revised whenever significant changes occur in the organisation or as a result of the findings of an accident or 'near miss' [124] investigation.

Workers' health and safety is protected in Europe through an approach based on assessing and managing risk. In order to carry out effective workplace risk assessment, all those involved require a clear understanding of the legal context, concepts, the process of assessing the risks and the roles of the main actors involved.

When taking action, the framework directive sets out the following general principles of prevention:

- avoiding risks;
- evaluating the risks which cannot be avoided;
- combating the risks at source;
- adapting the work to the individual, especially as regards the design of workplaces, the choice of work equipment and the choice of working and production methods, with a view, in particular, to alleviating monotonous work and work at a predetermined work rate and to reducing their effect on health;
- adapting to technical progress;
- replacing the dangerous with the non-dangerous or the less dangerous;
- developing a coherent overall prevention policy which covers technology, organisation of work, working conditions, social relationships and the influence of factors related to the working environment;
- giving collective protective measures priority over individual protective measures;
- giving appropriate instructions to the workers [125].

It is difficult for the management of a cleaning company to assess the risks related to the work environment of the purchasing organisation. Therefore the purchaser should be involved in this process so that these kinds of specific risks can be assessed, too.

124 A near miss is an unplanned event that did not result in injury, illness, or damage — but had the potential to do so.

125 Council Directive 89/391/EEC of 12 June 1989 on the introduction of measures to encourage improvements in the safety and health of workers at work Article 6 (http://eur lex.europa.eu/smartapi/cgi/sga_doc?smartapi!celexapi!prod!CELEXnumdoc&lg=EN&numdoc=389L0391&model=guichett).

Effective communication between the different parties is indispensable to identify all risks related to a certain cleaning job.

The example in this report of the cleaning of laboratories at the University of Edinburgh is an example of how purchasers can be involved in the risk assessment process. Purchasers might, for example, prepare instructions and procedures on how to clean the areas with risks related to their activities and work environment.

When risks and the related tasks are identified and quantified, measures have to be set in place to improve the working conditions for cleaners. The prevention hierarchy has always to be followed and, therefore, it is even better if prevention of risks is taken into account as early as the design phase. In France, a hotel undergoing renovation did just this, constructing model rooms so that cleaners could give feedback about certain risk factors before the final design was approved.

The list of hazards and risks below is not exhaustive, and it should be noted that workers may be exposed to a combination of hazards that could compound any harm that might occur.

6.4.1. Slips, trips and falls

Slips, trips and falls are a continual risk, particularly if carrying out 'wet work'. Slips, trips and falls are the most frequent causes of accidents in the cleaning sector. Some of these are trivial but some have grave consequences: broken bones, concussion, head injuries, even death.

Slips happen when there is too little friction between footwear and walking surface. Many factors can provoke a slip. Ice, oil, water, cleaning fluids, and other slippery substances are the common causes. Trips can be caused by changes in floor level (as little as 8 mm) or obstacles such as trailing cables or boxes. Falls are usually the result of slips and trips. But falls also occur without slipping or tripping. There are two basic types of falls: same-level falls and falls from height (e.g. due to improper use of ladders and scaffolding).

Factors identified as factors causing workers to slip or fall include poor floor conditions (e.g. wet floors), poor lighting, and temporary or fixed obstacles in the workplace (e.g. trailing cables).

Wet work, which covers cleaning activities where the skin is exposed to water for a prolonged time, not only increase the risk of skin problems in cleaners but also the risk of slips.

6.4.2. Exposure to hazardous substances in cleaning materials

The cleaning products used by workers can be unpleasant and, particularly when mixed, may cause harm. Products may contain or produce dangerous substances to which cleaners can be exposed through inhalation, skin and eye contact, or by ingestion. Some products may be highly flammable. Toxic gases can be formed if products are mixed: e.g. chlorine bleach mixed with acid or ammonia produces toxic gas, and certain dangerous substances can harm the health of pregnant workers and their unborn babies [126].

126 See EU-OSHA — European Agency for Safety and Health at Work E-fact 41 — Cleaners and dangerous substances 2008 (http://osha.europa.eu/en/publications/e-facts/efact41/view).

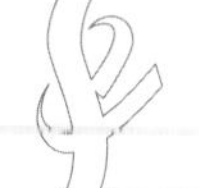

Cleaners can suffer from skin problems such as eczema and dermatitis as a result of using some cleaning materials, wet work, or handling waste material[127]. In addition, workers are at risk of injury by needlesticks or other sharp contaminated objects when emptying waste bins, in e.g. the healthcare sector or public areas. These accidents can cause infection with several viruses and bacteria. Cleaners should be informed about the risk and appropriate preventive measures[128].

6.4.3. Exposure to hazardous substances being cleaned

By the nature of the cleaning process, cleaning workers are exposed to unpleasant substances. These can vary from dirt, dust, and soot particulates to biological hazards including moulds, rodent droppings and human biological wastes.

6.4.4. Hazards and risks relating to psychosocial issues

Cleaning workers may work alone, which can mean that there are no emergency procedures in the event of an incident. The perceived status of cleaning workers and the composition of the workforce (female, possibly immigrant) may make them vulnerable to bullying or harassment. Violence, aggression, stress and unfavourable work organisation are often interrelated. Working alone and late at night can make cleaners vulnerable to violence and sexual harassment.

Unclear responsibilities, poor induction to the work, lack of training and few or no possibilities to communicate with colleagues, supervisors and client's employees may also be factors contributing to work-related stress. Monotonous and repetitive tasks and insecure employment positions can also be factors.

6.4.5. Risk of musculoskeletal disorders

Cleaning workers may be exposed to factors that increase their risk of musculoskeletal disorders (MSDs), including problems with the back, lower limb and upper limb disorders[129 130 131]. These may include:

- a lack of control over how they work;
- a heavy workload and restricted working times;
- unfavourable work schedules;
- lack of training in correct techniques;
- exposure to risk factors over long periods of time;

127 Messing, Karen, Indoor cleaning services, available online (http://www.ilo.org/encyclopedia/?doc&nd=857200403&nh=0&ssect=2).

128 See EU-OSHA — European Agency for Safety and Health at Work E-fact 40 — Risk assessment and needlestick injuries 2008 (http://osha.europa.eu/en/publications/e-facts/efact40).

129 Cabeças, J.M., Graça, L., Mendes, B., Gonçalves, M. 2005 Condições de trabalho de empregados de limpeza em instalações de serviços. ISHST — Instituto para a Segurança, Higiene e Saúde no Trabalho (Portuguese Institute for Occupational Health). Project report.

130 Woods, V., Buckle, P. 2006 'Musculoskeletal ill health amongst cleaners and recommendations for work organisational change', Int J Ind Ergon 36:61–72.

131 See EU-OSHA — European Agency for Safety and Health at Work E-fact 39 — Cleaners and musculoskeletal disorders 2008 (http://osha.europa.eu/en/publications/e-facts/efact39/view).

- carrying out physically demanding work, often in awkward positions, such as lifting furniture and carrying heavy loads;
- carrying out repetitive movements (e.g. mopping floors), often needing to employ force in the process;
- working in a non-ergonomic workplace (where no account has been taken of the needs of cleaning workers).

6.4.6. Risks relating to work equipment

This can include, for example, the trapping of fingers in machinery, or being exposed to an electric shock. Hazards associated with the equipment include:

- overextension
- falls from ladders
- heavy loads
- electric shock
- trips over cables [132].

Cleaners are confronted with the risk of electrical accidents when they work with powered equipment. Electrical accidents may be caused by defective machines or equipment, by faulty electric installations or by handling errors. Consequences of electrical hazards may be: electric shocks, electrocution, skin burns or fire. Use of work equipment in addition may expose cleaners to noise and vibrations.

132 See EU-OSHA — European Agency for Safety and Health at Work E-fact 38 — Work equipment, tools and cleaners 2008 (http://osha.europa.eu/en/publications/e-facts/efact38/view).

Table 67: Table of most common hazards, risks and related measures in the cleaning sector

Type of hazards	Subtypes	Preventive measures
Chemical hazards	■ Chemical substances in dirt, dust, soot particles	■ Train the workers in how to use, store and mix cleaning products safely. ■ Providing the workers with cleaning tools that attract dust instead of dispersing it.
	■ Hazardous substances within cleaning products ■ Wet work	■ Eliminate or substitute hazardous chemicals or wet work, e.g. by switching to dry or damp cleaning. ■ Provide SDS and safety instructions to enable professional or industrial users to take necessary health and safety precautions.
Biological hazards	■ Fungi, human excreta, blood and body fluids, bacteria, viruses, etc.	■ Make sure the employees wear respirators during work in a dusty area; ensure adequate ventilation. ■ Employees should wear personal protective equipment. ■ Cleaners who come in contact with biological hazards should wash or disinfect their hands.
Psychosocial hazards	■ Related to working time: cleaners mostly work outside normal office hours	■ Set objective targets, e.g. by using software like 'CleanNet'. ■ Make daytime cleaning possible by making some practical changes (e.g. vacuum cleaning early in the morning or using low-decibel vacuum cleaners to avoid disturbing the client). Involve all stakeholders when changing the working hours of the cleaners. Good planning and organisation is needed.
	■ Related to violence, harassment, and bullying	■ Have a 'zero tolerance' policy to bullying and harassment. ■ Provide mechanisms where incidents can be reported.
	■ Related to work organisation: lack of control over work and breaks, high workload and time pressure, working alone	■ Introduce team-based cleaning with different levels of autonomy for the workers. ■ This reduces the time the cleaner works alone; it increases responsibility at work to develop personal skills. ■ The reduction of the workload and the enrichment of the job content, team-based jobs, and combi-jobs (e.g. jobs that combine caretaking and cleaning) can be introduced to cope with the negative health outcomes.

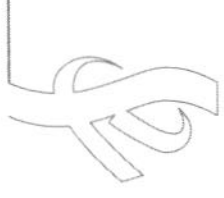

Type of hazards	Subtypes	Preventive measures
Physical hazards	Ergonomic hazards [133]: ■ poor working postures (e.g. reaching and stooping) ■ high application of forces (e.g. scrubbing, squeezing, moving and controlling (power) equipment) ■ repetitive movements (sometimes performed for up to one hour) and insufficient rest periods (all sub-sectors) ■ lifting and carrying loads (especially in industrial cleaning) ■ static work-loads/equipment (high pressure spraying, overhead cleaning) ■ working in confined space (public transport) ■ poor ergonomic design of the shape, size, adjustment and angle of handles ■ Poor ergonomic design of equipment in general	■ Consult during the procurement of cleaning tools and the design of buildings and furniture. Provide equipment and machines with adequate capacity, equipment that is adapted to the physical needs of the workers, enough workspace and essential accessories (e.g. gloves). ■ It is essential that purchasers take into account the particular requirements of the cleaners before the purchase. ■ The interior design of buildings should be adapted to facilitate cleaning work. Cables on the floors and behind desks obliging cleaners to squat and crawl to lift the cables while cleaning should be avoided. ■ Cleaners should be properly trained to use their equipment. ■ Employees should follow a structured training on use of equipment and health and safety, installation of equipment maintenance procedures, monitoring and early warning systems for musculoskeletal health problems, e.g. introduce a training concept such as 'Moving with Awareness'.
	■ Electrical hazards	■ Electrical equipment should naturally be maintained well and routinely checked, repaired or replaced, but in addition the cleaner should inspect the equipment for any damage before use.
	■ Noise, ambient or produced by cleaning equipment (such as vacuum cleaners)	■ Production of quieter machines. ■ Provision of personal hearing protection.
	■ Vibrations (caused by vibrating equipment)	■ Selection of tools that have minimal vibration. ■ Equipment should be properly used and well maintained.
	■ Slips, trips and falls	■ Adequate and regular floor cleaning is essential in controlling slips, trips and falls. However, the process of cleaning can itself lead to trips, slips and falls due to wet surfaces, obstacles during cleaning, electrical cables, etc. Slip-resistant flooring surfaces and proper working shoes are essential to avoid risks. Use cable-free machines.
	■ Thermal climate (high temperature and high relative humidity)	■ Cleaners should be instructed to recognise the symptoms of heat stress.
Work equipment	■ Ergonomic design of work equipment (e.g. its weight and length) ■ Safe design of work equipment (e.g. no accessible sharp parts, or 'hot spots'	■ Employers should provide their employees with properly designed equipment, which should accommodate the physical dimensions and strength of a wide range of potential users. ■ Employers should also provide appropriate personal protective equipment.

133 Kumar, R; Kumar S., 'Musculoskeletal risk factors in cleaning occupation — a literature review', Int J Ind Ergon April 2006. Munar Suard, L., Schiettecatte, E., Lebeer, G., De oorzaken van stress in de schoonmaaksector, Université Libre de Bruxelles, Institut de sociologie, 2003.

Make sure cleaners have the skills and knowledge to do their jobs safely 6.5.

Employers can provide their cleaning employees with state-of-the-art ergonomic equipment, but if the cleaners don't use it properly, it will be useless. Cleaners have to be provided with the knowledge and skills necessary to perform their jobs effectively and safely. Cleaners should be given information not only about the risks directly associated with the task being done (e.g. from the chemical cleaners being used), but also from the environment being cleaned (e.g. from hazardous substances in the location being cleaned). The training should raise the workers' awareness of the hazards and risks associated with cleaning, and there should be as much supervision as possible during training, so that supervisors can detect unsafe behaviour and correct it immediately.

Off-the-job training can be combined with on-the-job training to make sure that the cleaners not only have the knowledge but also can apply it. Off-the-job-training also provides an opportunity to address the risks related to the specific environment.

Take account of the employment structure in the cleaning sector 6.6.

One of the obstacles to prevention of risks among cleaners comes from the employment structure of the cleaning business. It is characterised by a large number of female workers who may be on part-time and/or short-term contracts, and who may either be migrant workers or drawn from ethnic minorities.

An example of how this can be managed is MAS, the cleaning company from the Netherlands that shows how employers can deal with the difficulties of working in a multicultural environment. An organisation with a high percentage of migrant workers will have to address communication problems if the cleaners cannot master the country's official language or speak a different language from their supervisor and colleagues. There might also be some cultural differences that need to be taken into account. The enterprise gives immigrants the chance to learn the country's official language by providing language courses. By doing so, they increase the cleaning workers' employability. They also offer their cleaners the chance to attend cleaning courses.

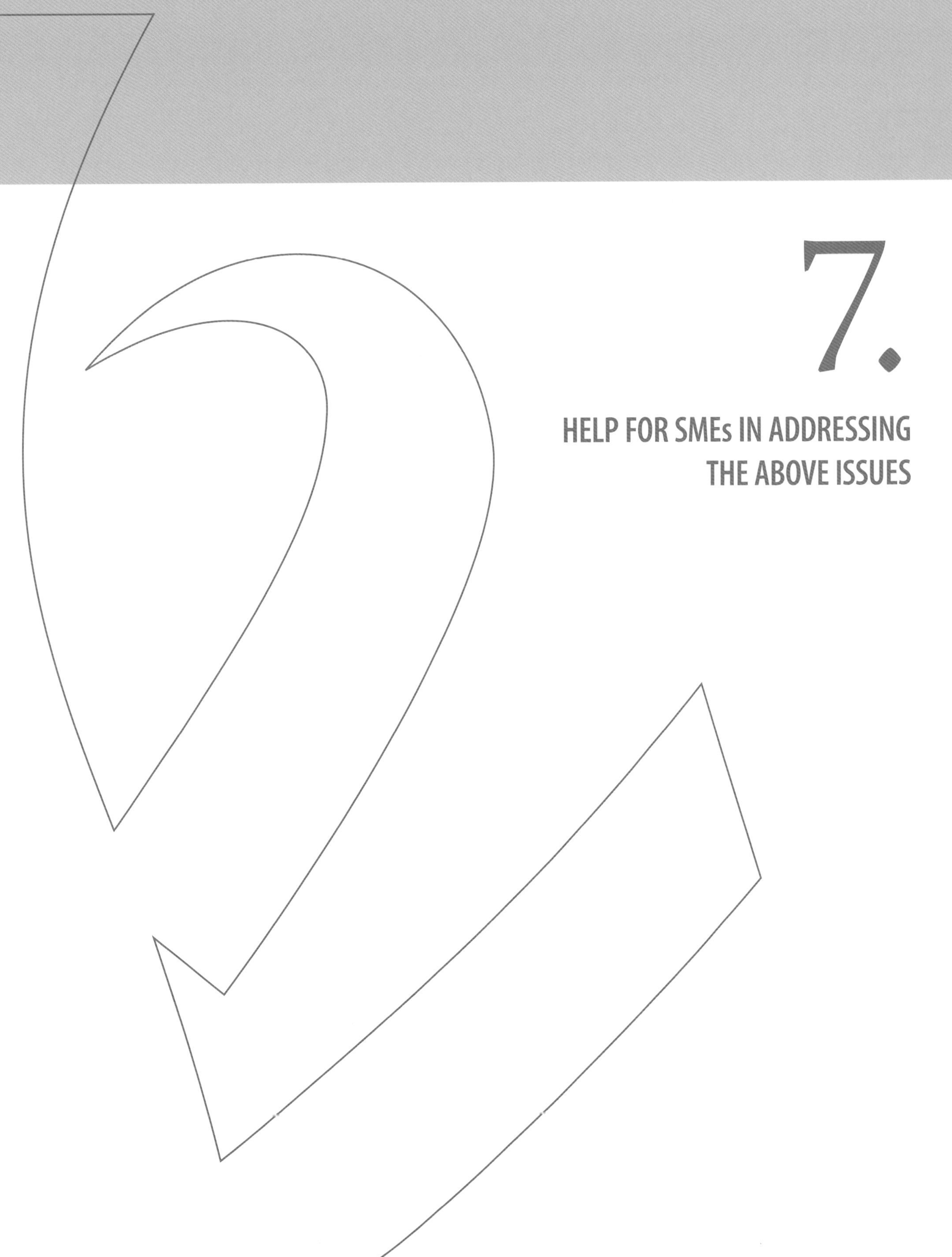

7.

HELP FOR SMEs IN ADDRESSING THE ABOVE ISSUES

Employers, employees of cleaning contractors and their respective associations could foster their cause by pointing out to procurement officials that procurement guidelines are available from esteemed institutions such as EUROCITIES and the European Social Dialogue. These guidelines offer objective procedures for including social, environmental and ethical criteria in purchasing decisions.

Daytime cleaning is common in some Scandinavian countries and has shown a number of benefits for clients and contractors alike. This report includes a detailed description based on experience from the Netherlands on how daytime cleaning can be introduced.

Service providers usually have to work in a number of different premises with a range of health and safety challenges, which underlines the importance of health and safety management systems. This report proves that these systems can and should be established in small and medium-sized enterprises as well as large companies, and presents an example from the State of Brandenberg in Germany. Both employers and employees recommended the system as it was not only beneficial to health and safety but also improved the economic situation of the company.

There should be proper communication channels between clients and service providers. It is also important that the procurement officials regularly receive feedback. The cleaners should be given a proper introduction to the job and have regular contact with their supervisors. Communication between all stakeholders is usually greatly improved when daytime cleaning is introduced.

Managing occupational health and safety requires the provision of appropriate training. There are different approaches, including a concept called Moving with Awareness [134] which builds on the practical experience of the cleaners, is practice oriented and has a slow and sensible approach to learning situations. The workers are sensitised to analyse the patterns of their own movements. Increased awareness allows them to consciously adapt their movements and working situations according to their own physical condition. This concept can easily be integrated into ongoing instructions and courses in SMEs as it also provides training for instructors. There is also a comprehensive training manual on occupational health available, issued by the European Social Dialogue in the cleaning sector.

There are a number of different ways of getting advice and exchanging opinions. Many of these Internet forums, networks, platforms, portals, databases, etc., are aimed at SMEs and also invite and encourage the cleaners themselves to take part so that their valuable experience can be put to good use. Examples in this report include websites from Germany, the Netherlands, Poland and the United Kingdom.

Many initiatives have developed guidelines for risk assessment in the cleaning sector. Four different approaches are detailed in this report, including from Belgium, Denmark, Germany, and Poland.

A great deal of guidance is available on the hazards and risks in the sector: technical rules and information have been compiled by government bodies, insurers, quality standards associations and academic researchers. They provide reliable advice based on long-standing experience in the sector. German guides, rules, and standards are particularly exhaustive.

134 See Huth, Elke, Moving with Awareness – An Ergonomic Approach to Training Cleaning Personnel, undated, unpublished, and (http://www.bewegungs-abc.de).

The organisation of work is an important topic in research projects like *Risk Assessment and Preventive Strategies in Cleaning Work*[135] and similar. These projects recommend daytime cleaning, job enrichment, team-based cleaning and more full-time jobs to tackle the sector-specific problems.

The cleaning sector is characterised by a large number of migrants, women, short-term employees, part-time workers, etc. This report presents an example from the Netherlands on how employers from cleaning organisations can deal with difficulties introduced by working in a multicultural environment by giving immigrants the possibility to learn the country's official language in special language courses.

135 Krueger, Detlef, Louhevaara, Veikko, Nilsen, Jette, Schneider, Thomas (eds), Risk Assessment and Preventive Strategies in Cleaning Work, Werkstattberichte aus Wissenschaft + Technik. Wb 13, Hamburg, 1997. The project is also presented online (http://www.rzbd.fh-hamburg.de/~prbiomed/risk_assessment.html and http://www.ttl.fi/Internet/English/Information/Electronic+journals/Tyoterveiset+journal/1999-02+Special+Issue/06.htm).

8. POINTS TO REMEMBER FOR DIFFERENT STAKEHOLDERS

8.1. Workers

- You are part of the cleaning industry, a dynamic service sector in the European Union.
- Constant advances in technology require equally similar advances in maintenance and cleaning procedures.
- Choosing the right cleaning, equipment and procedures is important to guarantee an extended life of buildings, fittings, industrial equipment, office equipment and furniture.
- Cleaning may take place in areas where sensitive information or dangerous equipment is stored, thus placing particular demands on the skills and integrity of cleaning personnel.
- You are an important part of the management system of your company. Pass on your experience, improve communication channels and enhance your skills by attending qualification courses in technical, health and safety aspects as well as language issues.
- Take part in risk assessment, discuss the necessary preventive methods and apply the measures decided upon.

8.2. Building occupants

Like any employee, cleaners need feedback. If you feel the job is not being done as well as it might be, contact the cleaners and tell them. But if the job is done satisfactorily, remember that cleaners also enjoy a word of praise.

See that the office or workshop is 'cleaner-friendly', i.e. all areas to be cleaned can be reached easily, the waste bins are not hidden away and there are no places where cleaners may trip or injure themselves.

8.3. Cleaning service providers

Make sure your employees are working in optimal conditions. To do this you must assess the risks related to the job and search for solutions. Communicate regularly with the client and their staff so that you are informed about the specific risks of the work environment. There are tailored guidelines available; use them. By improving the health and safety situation:

- health problems and absenteeism are reduced;
- appropriate machinery and equipment make the work much more effective;
- worker retention is increased and keeps experience in the company and assures quality of work.

In order to tackle the sector-specific problems, additional measures like daytime cleaning, job enrichment, team-based cleaning and more full-time jobs are recommended. Encourage your staff to attend courses to improve their skills and qualifications.

8.4. Procurers

The cheapest bid is certainly not always the best one. Make sure that your decision is based on social, environmental and ethical concerns in order to ensure a quality service and to improve the working conditions of the cleaners. Use procurement guides to help in the objective selection of the best service provider.

Make regular follow-up checks to verify that promises in the bids are adhered to after the provider starts the service. Establish communication channels with health and safety officials in your own company and at the service provider.

8.5. Safety and health professionals

A comprehensive training manual on occupational safety and health is available for the cleaning sector, issued by the European social partners. More specifically, special training concepts such as Moving with Awareness can be effective. There are many other guidelines available in Member States, and information is frequently available online for consultation. Fora also exist in which knowledge can be shared.

8.6. Architects, designers, manufacturers and suppliers

Ensure rooms are designed to be cleaner-friendly by measures including:

- providing enough space for cleaning procedures around toilets;
- keeping skirting boards small so that dust cannot settle on top;
- using furnishings and fabrics that do not attract and show dirt;
- discuss and test your equipment and cleaning agents with cleaning workers and appropriate experts.

European Agency for Safety and Health at Work

WORKING ENVIRONMENT INFORMATION

9.

SUMMARY

Procurement

- Good procurement practice can improve safety and health performance, and benefit companies in other ways as well.
- Guidelines on procurement are available covering all aspects (not just health and safety), and can be beneficial.
- The public sector can lead on procurement issues.

Safety and health management

- Occupational safety and health management is key to prevention and has business advantages.
- A holistic approach to protecting cleaners' safety and health is required; it may need to cover racism/language/disability/absenteeism/part-time working and other issues.
- Consultation with the workers is vital.
- It is possible to fit the job to the person and not vice versa.
- Clear guidelines are required for workers, supervisors and premises managers in the case of high-risk cleaning (e.g. laboratories).
- Risk assessment is important and the person carrying it out needs to be trained and knowledgeable.
- Good first-line supervision is key.

Cooperation with person in control of premises

- Persons in control of premises and workplace designers can make choices to reduce risks to workers.
- Identification of workers in high-risk work areas (e.g. hospitals) is important, and has to be done in conjunction with the person in charge of the premises.

Daytime cleaning

- Daytime cleaning is possible, with benefits to employers (e.g. reduced staff turnover).
- Offices (e.g. meeting rooms) are frequently empty at many times of day, allowing daytime cleaning.
- Daytime cleaning results in improved communication.

Training

- Integrated training helps promote diversity and safety and health, and can reduce absenteeism.
- Personal development, not just safety and health training, can bring wide-ranging benefits.
- Training promotion (e.g. through subsidies) can be effective.
- Including occupational safety and health in vocational training curricula can be beneficial.

Awareness and information dissemination

- Awareness-raising is important, as is provision of information on assessment and prevention.
- The Web is a good way to disseminate knowledge.
- Provision of tools (e.g. for risk assessment) can be effective.

- An IT infrastructure can aid knowledge exchange between experts and others.
- Involvement of workers in campaigns raises awareness.

Policy level

- Integration of marginal workforce through action relating to 'grey' employment, language/cultural issues is important.
- Tackling racism and discrimination can help prevent psychosocial risks to workers and benefit business (e.g. through reduced absenteeism).
- Research into risks in the cleaning sector is ongoing and still required.

Social dialogue and cooperation

- A common approach with social partners is most effective.
- A good image for the industry can bring safety and health benefits.
- Sharing knowledge between social partners, inspectorates, etc., can be beneficial.

10.

ANNEXES

10.1. Annex — List of abbreviations

Abbreviation	Description
AA	Amt für Arbeitsschutz Hamburg (Germany)
ABSU	Belgian employers association in the cleaning sector
ABVV	Belgian trade union
ACV	Belgian trade union
AMAT	Asociación de Mutuas de Accidentes de Trabajo y enfermedades Profesionales de la Seguridad Social (Spain)
AMS	Arbeitsschutz-Managementsystem (Germany)
AUVA	Austrian Social Insurance for Occupational Risks
BBC	Committee in the Netherlands that drew up the work covenant for the cleaning industry
BCC	British Cleaning Council (UK)
BG	Berufsgenossenschafen — Institutions for statutory accident insurance and prevention (Germany); an 'I' after a document indicates 'information' and 'R' indicates 'rule'
BG BAHNEN	Berufsgenossenschafen der Strassen, U-Bahnen und Eisenbahnen (Germany)
BG BAU	Institute for Statutory Accident Insurance and Prevention of the Building Industry (Germany)
BICSc	British Institute of Cleaning Services (UK)
BIOMED	Biomedical and Health Research Programme
CAC	Czech Association of Cleaning
CARPE	Cities As Responsible Purchasers in Europe
CECOP	European Confederation of Workers Cooperatives, Social Cooperatives, and Participative Enterprises
CEMOC	Occupational Medicine Centre (Italy)
CEN	Committee on Standardisation
CIFoP	Centré Interuniversitaire de Formation Permanente
CIOP — PIB	Central Institute for Labour Protection — National Research Institute (Poland)
CLIF	Cleaning Industry Liaison Forum (UK)
CNV BedrijvenBond	Dutch trade union
COSHH	Control of Substances Hazardous to Health (UK)
CRAMIF	Caisse Régionale d'Assurance Maladie d'Ille de France (France)
CSQ	Czech Society for Quality
CSS	Centre de Sociologie de la Santé, ULB (Belgium)
DIN	German Standard Organisation
EDF	European Disability Forum
EEB	European Environmental Bureau
EFCI/FENI	European Federation of Cleaning Industries
ELINYAE	Hellenic Institute of Occupational Health and Safety (Greece)
EPSU	European Federation of Public Service Unions
ESF	European Social Fund (UK)
ETUC	European Trade Union Confederation
EU	European Union
EU-OSHA	EU-OSHA — European Agency for Safety and Health at Work

Abbreviation	Description
FGÖ	Foundation Health Austria
FLEN	Fédération Luxembourgeoise des Entreprises de nettoyage de bâtiments
FNV Bondgenoten	Dutch trade union
GISBAU	Gefahrstoff-Informationssystem der BG BAU (Germany)
HSE	Health and Safety Executive (UK)
HSK	Horst Schmidt Klinik (Germany)
HVBG	Hauptverband der gewerblichen Berufsgenossenschafen
IDEWE	The largest Belgian occupational health service
IKA	Association of Public Purchasers (Denmark)
ILO	International Labour Organisation
INAIL	Italian Worker's Compensation Authority
ISCO	International Standard Classification for Occupations
ISO	International Standard Organisation
ISTAS	Instituto Sindical de Trabajo Ambiente y Salud (Spain)
KMK	Die Ständige Konferenz der Kultusminister der Länder in der Bundesrepublik Deutschland (Kurzform: Kultusministerkonferenz)
LAEK	Account for Employment and Vocational Training (Greece)
LAfA	State Institute for Occupational Safety and Health of North Rhine-Westphalia
LCGB	Lëtzebuerger Chrëschtleche Gewerkschaftsbond (Fédération des syndicats chrétiens luxembourgeois), Luxembourg trade union
MAS	Multicultural Amsterdam Cleaning Company (Netherlands)
MSDs	Musculoskeletal disorders
NAGD	Standardisation Committee 'Gebrauchstauglichkeit und Dienstleistungen'
NIOSH	National Institute for Occupational Safety and Health (USA)
NLF	German guideline for occupational health and safety management systems
NÖGKK	Lower Austria Regional Health Insurance
OCRA Checklist	A means of evaluating risks of MSDs
OGNL	Confédération Syndicale Indépendante du Luxembourg (Onofhängege Gewerkschaftsbond Lëtzebuerg), Luxembourg trade union
OSB	Dutch employers' association for cleaning and company services
OSE	Hellenic Railways Organisation (Greece)
PAC	Polish Cleaning Association (Poland)
PROVIKMO	The external services for prevention and protection at work (Belgium)
RAL	German Institute for Quality Assurance and Certifications
SEFMEP	Prevention service for the construction sector (Belgium)
SIPTU	Services, Industrial, Professional, and Technical Union, Ireland
SME	Small and medium-sized enterprise
Sobane	Screening, Observation, Analysis, and Expertise programme (Belgium)
SPT	Association of Danish Manufacturers and Importers of Soap, Detergents, Perfume, Cosmetics, and Chemical Technical products
SSDC	Sectoral Social Dialogue
SZW	Dutch Ministry of Social Affairs and Employment
TLA	Three letter acronym
UIL	Uniona Italiana de Lavore (Italy)
UK	United Kingdom
ULB	Université Libre de Bruxelles (Belgium)
USA	United States of America
ZDB	Zentralverband des Deutschen Baugewerbes (national Association of German Builders)

10.2. Annex — Relevant European directives

- Council Directive 89/391/EEC of 12 June 1989, framework Directive — this general directive on the introduction of measures to encourage improvements in the safety and health of workers obliges the employer to take the necessary measures to ensure the safety and health of the workers in all aspects of their work.
- Council Directive 89/654/EEC of 30 November 1989, Workplace Directive — this directive concerns the minimum safety and health requirements for both workplaces in use and workplaces used for the first time. These requirements are extensively described in the annexes of the directive.
- Council Directive 89/655/EEC of 30 November 1989, Work Equipment Directive — concerning the requirements for use of work equipment (e.g. tools and machines).
- Council Directive 89/656/EEC of 30 November 1989, PPE Directive — all personal protective equipment must take account of ergonomic requirements and the worker's state of health and fit the wearer correctly after any necessary adjustment.
- Council Directive 90/269/EEC of 29 May 1990, Manual Handling Directive — the need for manual handling of loads should be avoided, otherwise the handling should be properly organised and the workers properly trained.
- Council Directive 98/24/EC of 7 April 1998 on the protection of the health and safety of workers from the risks related to chemical agents at work (14th individual directive within the meaning of Article 16(1) of Directive 89/391/EEC).
- Directive 2000/54/EC of the European Parliament and of the Council of 18 September 2000, Biological Agents Directive — the aim of this directive is to establish minimum requirements to provide workers exposed to biological agents at work with a better level of safety and health protection.
- Directive 2002/44/EC of the European Parliament and of the Council of 25 June 2002, Vibrations Directive — the exposure of workers to the risks arising from vibration.
- Council Directive 91/383/EEC of 29 July 1991, Temporary Worker Directive — the aim of this directive is to implement supplementary provisions to ensure that temporary workers enjoy the same level of protection as other workers.
- Council Directive 94/33/EC of 22 June 1994, Young Workers Directive — places responsibilities on employers to ensure that the risks to young workers are minimised by making the risk assessment before they begin their work.
- Council Directive 93/104/EC of 23 November 1993, Working Time — the aims of the directive are to adopt minimum requirements covering certain aspects of the organisation of working time connected with workers' health and safety.
- Directive 98/37/EC of the European Parliament and of the Council of 22 June 1998, Supply of Machinery Directive — requirements on the supply of machinery for use at work.
- Directive 2004/17/EC of the European Parliament and of the Council of 31 March 2004, Utilities Directive — coordinating the procurement procedures of entities operating in the water, energy and transport sectors.

- Directive 2004/18/EC of the European Parliament and of the Council of 31 March 2004, Classic Directive — concerning the coordination of procedures for the award of public works contracts.

Annex — Material from the ILO 10.3.

The ILO has published a range of conventions, recommendations and codes of practice that affect cleaners.

10.3.1. Conventions

- C155 Occupational Safety and Health Convention, 1981
- C171 Night Work Convention, 1990
- C172 Working Conditions (Hotels and Restaurants) Convention, 1991
- C131 Minimum Wage Fixing Convention with Special Reference to Developing Countries, 1970
- C100 Equal Remuneration Convention for Men and Women Workers for Work of Equal Value, 1951
- C111 Convention concerning Discrimination in Respect of Employment and Occupation, 1958
- C143 Convention concerning Migrants in Abusive Conditions and the Promotion of Equality of Opportunity and Treatment of Migrant Workers, 1975
- C 170 Convention concerning Safety in the use of Chemicals at Work

10.3.2. Recommendations

- R164 Occupational Safety and Health Recommendation, 1981
- R178 Night Work Recommendation, 1990
- R179 Working Conditions (Hotels and Restaurants) Recommendation, 1991
- R135 Minimum Wage Fixing Recommendation, 1970
- R90 Equal Remuneration Recommendation, 1951
- R111 Discrimination (Employment and Occupation) Recommendation, 1958
- R151 Migrant Workers Recommendation, 1975
- R177 Recommendation concerning Safety in the use of Chemicals at Work
- R117 Vocational Training Recommendation, 1962

10.3.3. Codes of Practice

- Workplace violence in services sectors and measures to combat this phenomenon, 2003
- Guidelines on Occupational Safety and Health Management Systems, 2001.
- Safety in the Use of Chemicals at Work, 1993 (supporting the respective convention and recommendation)

10.4. Annex — Relevant standards

- ISO 2631:2001 Mechanical vibration and shock — Evaluation of human exposure to whole-body vibration
- ISO 5349:1986 Mechanical vibration — Guidelines for the measurement and the assessment of human exposure to hand-transmitted vibration
- EN 14253:2003 Mechanical vibration — Measurement and calculation of occupational exposure to whole-body vibration with reference to health — Practical guidance
- ISO 5805:1997 Mechanical vibration and shock — Human exposure — Vocabulary
- prEN ISO 20643 Hand-transmitted vibration from hand-held or hand-guided machinery — Measurement of vibration at the grip surface (ISO/DIS 20643:2002)
- ISO 8662:1988 Hand-held portable power tools — Measurement of vibrations at the handle

10.5. Bibliography

- Abott, D., Caring for cleaners: Health and Safety at work, reproduced with permission of LexisNexis, 2004 (http://www.enricosmog.com/resources/cleaners.pdf).
- Bena, A., Mamo, A., Marinacci, C., Pasqualini, O., Tomaino, A., Costa, G., 'Infortuni ripetuti, rischio per professioni in Italia negli anni novanta' (Risk of repeated injuries by economic activity in Italy in the 1990s), Med Lav 96, Suppl pp. 116–126, 2005 (Italian) (http://www.dors.it/alleg/0201/09-bena.pdf).
- BG BAU (Berufsgenossenschaft der Bauwirtschaft), Prävention kompakt — Gebäudereiniger, Berufsgenossenschaft der Bauwirtschaft, 2005 (http://www.gisbau.de/service/brosch/Gebaeudereiniger.pdf).
- Cabeças, J.M., Graça, L., Mendes, B., Gonçalves, M., Condições de trabalho de empregados de limpeza em instalações de services, ISHST — Instituto para a Segurança, Higiene e Saúde no Trabalho (Portuguese Institute for Occupational Health). Project report, 2005.
- Comcare, Slips Trips and Falls, Australian government, rehabilitation guide, 2004 (http://www.comcare.gov.au/).
- DAK-BGW, Arbeitsbedingungen und Gesundheit von Pflegekräften in der Bundesrepublik, DAK-BGW Krankenpflegereport 2000 (http://www.dak.de/content/files/krpflrep.doc).
- EFCI (European Federation of Cleaning Industries), Health & Safety in the office cleaning sector (http://www.feni.be/index.php?id=19&L=0).

- EFCI (European Federation of Cleaning Industries), The cleaning sector in Europe, EFCI Survey, 2006 (http://www.feni.be/index.php?id=18).
- Eurofound, 'Migrants in Europe face severe challenges', Eurofound News May 2007 (http://www.eurofound.europa.eu/press/eurofoundnews/2007/may/newsletter3.htm).
- EU-OSHA — European Agency for Safety and Health at Work, Gender issues in safety and health at work — A review, Report TE5103786ENC, p. 37, 2003 (http://osha.europa.eu/publications/reports/209).
- EU-OSHA — European Agency for Safety and Health at Work, How to Reduce Workplace Accidents, Factsheet 20, 2001b (http://osha.europa.eu/publications/factsheets/20/index.htm?set_language=en).
- EU-OSHA — European Agency for Safety and Health at Work, Preventing accidents at work magazine, No 4, pp. 23–24, 2001a (http://osha.europa.eu/publications/magazine/4/?set_language=de).
- EU-OSHA — European Agency for Safety and Health at Work, Elimination and substitution of dangerous substances, Factsheet 34, (http://osha.europa.eu/publications/factsheets/34/factsheetsn34-en.pdf).
- Finnish Association of Cleaning Technology, Cleaning Manual, Karpprint Ky, Vihti Finland, 1998.
- Flyvholm, M., Mygind, K., Sell, L., Jensen, A., Jepsen, K., 'A randomised controlled intervention study on prevention of work related skin problems among gut cleaners in swine slaughterhouses', Occup Environ Med. 62(9), Sept. 2005, pp. 642–649.
- Gamperiene, M., Nygård, J., Brage, S., Bjerkedal, T., Bruusgaard, D., 'Duration of employment is not a predictor of disability of cleaners: a longitudinal study', Scand J Public Health 31(1), 2003, pp. 63–68.
- Gamperiene, M., Nygård, J., Sandanger, I., Wærsted, M., Bruusgaard, D., 'The impact of psychosocial and organisational working conditions on the mental health of female cleaning personnel in Norway', J Occup Med Toxicol 1(1), November 2006 (http://www.occup-med.com/content/1/1/24).
- GMB — Britain's General Union, Health and Safety for Cleaners — A GMB Guide (http://www.gmb.org.uk/Templates/PublicationItems.asp?NodeID=91047).
- Hoods, V., Buckle, P., Haisman, M., Musculoskeletal Health of Cleaners, Robens Centre for Health Ergonomics, University of Surrey, 1999 (http://www.hse.gov.uk/research/crr_pdf/1999/CRR99215.pdf).
- HSE — Health and Safety Executive, Caring for cleaners. Guidance and case studies on how to prevent musculoskeletal disorders, HSG234, ISBN 0-7176-2682-2 (http://www.hse.gov.uk/press/2003/e03078.htm).
- HSE — Health and Safety Executive, Safe use of cleaning chemicals in the hospitality industry (http://www.hse.gov.uk/pubns/cais22.pdf).
- HSE, Slips and trips in the healthcare services, Health Services Sheet No 2, 2003 (http://www.hse.gov.uk/pubns/hsis2.pdf).
- HSE, Slips and trips: The importance of floor cleaning, HSE information sheet Slips and Trips 2, 2005 (http://www.hse.gov.uk/pubns/web/slips02.pdf).
- Huth, Elke, Arbeitsfelder: Arbeits- und Gesundheitsschutz in der Reinigung, Reinigungs- und Hygiene — Technik, Facility Management (http://www.bewegungs-abc.de/haupt.htm).
- Huth, Elke, Krueger, Detlef, Kopf, Thomas, Gestaltung Gesunder Artbeitsbedingungen: Projekt Reinigung, Gesundheitsförderung für die Mitarbeiterinnen des Referates Technik und Hausverwaltung im Hygiene Institut Hamburg, Fachhochschule Hamburg, 2001.

- Huth, Elke, Krueger, Detlef, Zorzi, Gerlinde, Gesundheitsförderung im Krankenhausbetrieb — Funktionsbereich Reinigung, Abschlußbericht, Fachhochschule Hamburg, 1996.
- ILO, Gender issues — Transport and General Workers' Union Guide to Women's Health & Safety, SafeWork, Chapter 4: Cleaning, 2003 (http://www.ilo.org/public/english/protection/safework/gender/trade_union/).
- INRS — Institut National de Recherche et de Securite, Les entreprises de propreté, Prévention des risques, Reference ED818, 1998 (http://www.inrs.fr/htm/les_entreprises_de_proprete_prevention_des_risques.html).
- ISTAS — Instituto Sindical de Trabajo, Ambiente y Salud, Fichas internacionales de datos de seguridad (http://www.istas.net/webistas/abreenlace.asp?idenlace=1570).
- Krueger, Detlef, Louhevaara, Veikko, Nilsen, Jette, Schneider, Thomas (eds) Risk Assessment and Preventive Strategies in Cleaning Work. Werkstattberichte aus Wissenschaft + Technik. Wb 13. Hamburg 1997.
- Kumar, R., Chaikumarn, M., Lundberg, J., 'Participatory ergonomics and an evaluation of a low-cost improvement effect on cleaners' working posture', Int J Occup Saf Ergon. 11(2), 2005, pp. 203–210.
- Laursen, B., Søgaard, K., Sjøgaard, G., 'Biomechanical model predicting electromyographic activity in three shoulder muscles from 3D kinematics and external forces during cleaning work', Clin Biomech (Bristol, Avon), 18(4), May 2003, pp. 287–295.
- Lorenzo Munar Suard, Guy Lebeer, Health & safety in the office cleaning sector — European manual for employees, Centre de Sociologie de la Santé of the Université Libre de Bruxelles (ULB) and the Centre de Diffusion de la Culture Sanitaire a.s.b.l., project partners uni-Europa and EFCI.
- Manning, D.P., 'Deaths and injuries caused by slipping, tripping and falling', Ergonomics 26(1), pp. 3–9.
- Massin, N., Hecht, G., Ambroise, D., Héry, M., Toamain, J., Hubert, G., Dorotte, M., Bianchi, B., 'Respiratory symptoms and bronchial responsiveness among cleaning and disinfecting workers in the food industry', Occup Environ Med. 64(2), Feb 2007, pp. 75–81.
- Messing, Karen, Indoor cleaning services (http://www.ilo.org).
- Mondelli, M., et al., 'Carpal tunnel syndrome and ulnar neuropathy at the elbow in floor cleaners', Neurophysiol Clin. 36(4), Jul–Aug 2006, pp. 245–253.
- Norddeutsche Metall BG, 'Stolper und Rutschunfälle ausschließen', Gesund + Sicher No 9, 2000 (http://www.nmbg.de/files/54/Stolpern_Rutschen.pdf).
- Scherzer, T., Rugulies, R., Krause, N., 'Work-related pain and injury and barriers to workers' compensation among Las Vegas hotel room cleaners', Am J Public Health 95(3), Mar 2005, pp. 483–488 (http://www.pubmedcentral.nih.gov/articlerender.fcgi?artid=1449206).
- UNI — Union Network International, Health and Safety in the office cleaning sector — European manual for employees, 2000 (http://www.union-network.org/UNIsite/Sectors/Property_Services/Cleaning/CleaningManual.htm).
- Vogel, Laurent, 'The TUTB study on gender sensitivity in occupational safety and health: some results and their implications', in EU-OSHA — European Agency for Safety and Health at Work Mainstreaming gender into occupational safety and health, proceedings of a seminar organised in Brussels on 15 June 2004, p.17 (http://osha.europa.eu/publications/reports/6805688).

- Woods, V., Buckle, P., Haisman M., Musculoskeletal health of cleaners, Robens Centre for Health and Ergonomics for the Health and Safety Executive and UNISON, HSE Books, 1999 (http://www.hse.gov.uk/research/crr_pdf/1999/CRR99215.pdf).
- Zock, J., et al., 'Asthma risk, cleaning activities and use of specific cleaning products among Spanish indoor cleaners', Scand J Work Environ Health 27(1), Feb 2001, pp. 76–81.

European Commission

Preventing harm to cleaning workers

Luxembourg: Office for Official Publications of the European Communities

2009 — 225 pp. — 21 x 29.7 cm

ISBN 978-92-9191-259-9

Price (excluding VAT) in Luxembourg: EUR 15